WHAT A YEAR IT WAS!
1958

A walk back in time to revisit
what life was like in the year that
has special meaning for you...

*Congratulations
and
Best Wishes*

To

From

DEDICATION

To My Daughter Laurie Whose Support, Commitment And Endless Hours Of Hard Work Made This Book Possible.

Designer • Peter Hess
Research and Production Supervisor • Laurie Cohn

CONTENTS

Politics
AND World Events

ALASKA WINS STATEHOOD

Celebrations break out all over as Alaska finally wins statehood.

Alaskans celebrate with an enthusiasm recalling "Sourdough" days.

 **A** new state twice as large as Texas joins the union.

A bright new star is added to the 48.

Vice President Richard Nixon and his wife Pat arrive in Caracas, Venezuela, on their goodwill tour of South America.

In a shocking climax to his tour, Mr. Nixon is attacked by a hostile anti-American mob angry over the political and economic policies of their country. Eisenhower sends troops to Caribbean to insure Nixon's safety.

Earlier, Communist-led mobs in Peru had stoned the Vice President, shouting "out with Nixon."

WHAT A YEAR IT WAS!

Demonstrators carry signs urging the closing of American air bases as well as proposed missile sites.

England's Communist Party Stages A
"YANKS GO HOME DAY"

This parade consists primarily of Communists and British Fascists.

NEW Vendo Coffee Maker makes the BIG difference!

You get a cup of *real* coffee, always fresh and flavorful, because it's brewed in small batches right in the vacuum packed can. The Vendo is the first . . . and only automatic coffee vender to use a new vacuum packed can each time as the brewing chamber. It serves coffee as you like it—black, with fresh cream or sugar, or any combination. Delicious hot chocolate, too.

Tear out this page and ask your employer today to call a Vending Operator about a Vendo Coffee Maker.

the BIG difference
The Vendo uses the same top quality coffee you buy—vacuum packed in ¼-lb. cans by all nationally known coffee roasters. Mail the coupon today.

The Vendo Company   (Mail on
7401 East 12th Street   your letterhead)
Kansas City 26, Missouri

Please send me complete information about how the new VENDO Coffee Maker can be used in our plant, office or building. I am also interested in

☐ Coca-Cola * ☐ Milk ☐ Ice Cream
☐ Free Coffee Demonstration ☐ ....

Name...Title.....................
Firm...
Address...
City...........................Zone......State.....................
We have ....employees. * TRADEMARK ®

Vendo for On-the-Spot Refreshment

Better buy by Brand Names ▶ BRAND NAMES WEEK

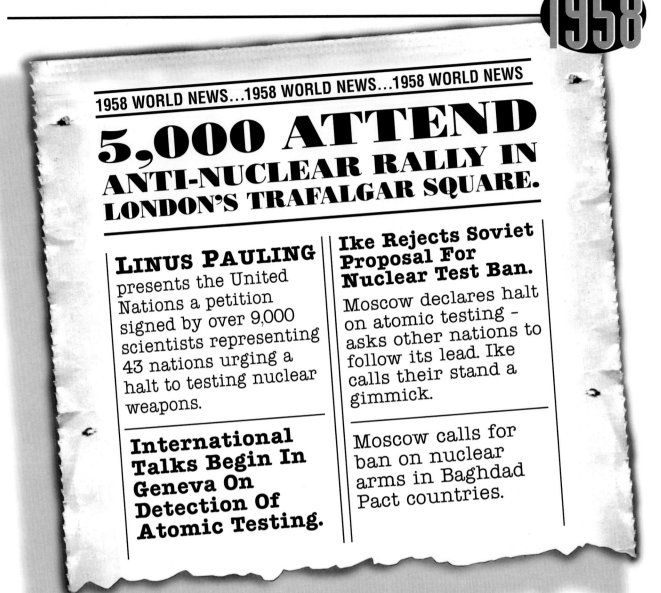

5,000 ATTEND
ANTI-NUCLEAR RALLY IN LONDON'S TRAFALGAR SQUARE.

LINUS PAULING

presents the United Nations a petition signed by over 9,000 scientists representing 43 nations urging a halt to testing nuclear weapons.

International Talks Begin In Geneva On Detection Of Atomic Testing.

Ike Rejects Soviet Proposal For Nuclear Test Ban.

Moscow declares halt on atomic testing - asks other nations to follow its lead. Ike calls their stand a gimmick.

Moscow calls for ban on nuclear arms in Baghdad Pact countries.

GERMANY'S Chancellor Adenauer defers to NATO on nuclear arms in West Germany.

At meetings held in Geneva, the United States, Great Britain and the Soviets reach an agreement on the draft of a Nuclear Test Ban.

Denmark Bars Entry Of U.S. Nuclear Sub Skate As An Atomic Hazard.

AEC Reports U.S.S.R. Resumed Atomic Testing In Arctic.

1958

Charles de Gaulle Named Premiere Of France After His Country Comes To The Brink Of Civil War Over Algerian Crisis

De Gaulle asks for and is granted exceptional powers and declares a six-month rule by decree as he prepares a new constitution for France.

The Fifth Republic comes into being with an overwhelming Gaullist majority in the new National Assembly.

Once again Charles de Gaulle is his nation's man of destiny.

Destruction In Tunisia By French Raids

The crisis in Franco-Tunisian relations are only slightly abated.

The blockade on 15,000 French troops remaining in the country.

Although both nations agree to put off a Security Council debate, France begins clearing a 15-mile wide buffer zone on her side of the Algerian border *(below left)* and Tunisia permits limited shipment of food to French troops.

1958

RUSSIA

NIKITA KHRUSHCHEV AND MAO TSE-TUNG MEET IN PEKING FOR TALKS. SOVIET LEADER ASKS IKE TO RECOGNIZE PEKING.

U.S.S.R. Grants Loan To The United Arab Republic For Construction Of The Aswan Dam.

New Soviet Ambassador Mikhail Menshikov Arrives In Washington.

Soviet Diplomat Nikolai Kurochkin Expelled From U.S. As Spy.

CHINA

Communist China Sinks Taiwan Transport Being Escorted By U.S.

Taiwan Shoots Down Ten MIG-17s.

Communist Chinese Bombard Quemoy With 38,000 Shells.

Chinese government executes peasants unwilling to participate in its "Great Leap Forward" commune program designed to help solve China's economy.

Communist China suspends trade relations with Japan because of Japan's hostile attitude toward China.

U.S. reaffirms refusal to recognize Red China.

Chou En-lai Resigns As Foreign Minister Of China.

EUROPEAN COMMON MARKET IS CREATED.

142 representatives from 6 Western European countries meet in Strasbourg, France for the first session of the European Parliamentary Assembly.

Field Marshall Viscount Montgomery Retires As NATO Deputy Supreme Commander In Europe.

AYUB KHAN ELECTED PRIME MINISTER OF PAKISTAN.

JORDAN AND IRAQ SIGN PACT.

JORDAN UNCOVERS LARGE PRO-NASSER SPY RING.

French Sudan in West Africa proclaims itself an autonomous republic within the French community.

Nasser BECOMES PRESIDENT OF NEWLY FORMED UNITED ARAB REPUBLIC.

In response to a formal request for U.S. intervention by President Cahmoun, U.S. Marines land on beaches south of Beirut, Lebanon.

THE DINAR, A NEW MONETARY UNIT, IS INTRODUCED BY TUNISIA.

CUBA

France

DE GAULLE ELECTED PRESIDENT OF FRANCE BY 79.2% OF THE VOTERS.

CRIPPLED BY 24-HOUR STRIKE OF PUBLIC WORKERS.

FRENCH LEFTISTS HOLD HUGE PROTEST IN SUPPORT OF REPUBLICAN GOVERNMENT.

French government calls for additional Gendarmerie, censors the press and bans public assemblies in Paris.

PREMIER PIERRE PFLIMLIN DECREES FULL PRESS CENSORSHIP IN ALGIERS.

Concerned that the French Cabinet will bow to demands of Algerian Nationalists and give up fight for French colonialism, thousands of angry Frenchmen storm streets in Algeria seizing French government buildings in protest over Premier Pierre Pfimlin's policies.

Imre Nagy Executed In Hungary After Secret Trial.

Ferenc Munnich Replaces Janos Kadar As Premier Of Hungary.

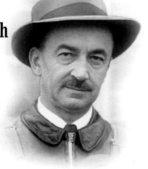

FIDEL CASTRO BEGINS "TOTAL WAR" AGAINST THE BATISTA GOVERNMENT IN CUBA.

Cuban Rebels Raid Port Area Of Manzanillo.

35 New Yorkers Are Seized On Way To Join Castro Rebels In Cuba.

Argentine Auto Race Champ Juan Manuel Fangio Seized By Cuban Rebels.

CUBAN PRESIDENT BATISTA SUSPENDS CONSTITUTIONAL RIGHTS TO FIGHT REBELS.

30 Officers Arrested In Cuba For Refusing To Join Offensive Against Rebels.

President Batista's sons arrive in New York declaring the fall of Cuba is imminent.

Florida Customs Agents Arrest 31 Heavily Armed People On Boat Headed For Cuba.

In Havana, Batista Declares Cubans May Kill Inciters.

CUBAN REBELS RELEASE LAST OF U.S. SERVICEMEN HELD.

Cuban forces led by Fidel Castro seize 28 U.S. Navy personnel, mostly Marines, near Guantanamo, the American naval base. The rebels claim they were retaliating against the U.S. for aiding Batista forces.

Castro announces that candidates for the November 3rd elections will be executed for treason. Warns U.S. to not interfere with revolt.

Former President of Cuba Carlos Prio Socarras is arrested in Miami on charges that he violated the Neutrality Laws of the United States.

Columbia's 9-Year State Of Siege Lifted By President Albert Lleras.

1958

Moshe Dayan
Resigns As Israeli Army Commander.

ISRAEL
Celebrates 10th Anniversary With Military Parade.

Women Protesters Attacked By Police With Machetes In Caracas.

700 seized under martial law in Argentina in plot to overthrow the government.

In the first free election in 30 years, Arturo Frondizi is elected President of Argentina.

Marshal Tito Elected President Of Yugoslavia For A Third Term.

Greek Rebels Call Truce With Turks And British.
Greek government announces severance of all military ties with Turkey under NATO's Southeast Europe command.

Princess Margaret
Inaugurates First Parliament Of West Indies Federation.

Haiti's President Francois Duvalier Helps Put Down Revolt.

New African republics proclaimed in Central Africa, Nigeria, Upper Volta, Ivory Coast and Dahomey. First Conference of Independent African States held in Ghana.

General Thanom Kittikachorn Named Prime Minister Of Thailand.

Canada And U.S.

Establish The Joint North American Air Defense Command (NORAD) Headquartered In Colorado Springs.

Voters give conservative John Diefenbaker the biggest parliamentary majority in Canadian history. Lester Pearson new leader of the Liberals.

The U.S. and Great Britain agree to send 50 jets to Iran, Jordan and Lebanon.

AT THE HAGUE, BENELUX COUNTRIES SIGN TREATY ABOLISHING 97% OF TRADE CURBS.

HOLLAND NATIONALIZES BANKING.

WHAT A YEAR IT WAS!

"Perfect Playback" lets you make changes *naturally*—just say it over the better way!

"Perfect Playback" gives her correction-free dictation—speeds letter-perfect transcription!

Stenocord with **"PERFECT PLAYBACK"** gives you more exclusive advantages than any other dictating machine!

Once you try this wonderful new way to dictate you'll never go back to needle-type machines.

Stenocord's Magnetic Belt makes dictating so much simpler, executives ask us: "Why didn't somebody think of this *years ago?*" The fact is, "Perfect Playback" combines a *number* of new and important advances in electronics — including new magnetic clarity of voice reproduction, simpler basic design and construction. It's a major advance in modern dictation.

Stenocord lets you make

MAGNETIC BELT—mailable, filable, re-usable.

changes and improvements *automatically*, as naturally as you do in face-to-face conversation. No need to make notes warning your secretary that you changed your mind. And at the touch of a thumb *you* can listen to *perfect playback.*

Your secretary will welcome this *correction-free dictation.* No more typing rough drafts. No more listening through "what he didn't want to say." She will type smoothly, serenely and much more swiftly with *perfect playback.*

Mail the coupon. Find out for yourself why business men in 39 countries are becoming Stenocord *addicts* as well as users.

Stenocord ®

SERIES 400

Sold and serviced in 39 countries of the free world

- **MAIL COUPON TODAY** -

STENOCORD DIVISION, Pacific Instruments Corporation, Dept. B-58, 7046 Hollywood Boulevard, Los Angeles 28, Calif.

Please send me the facts on "Perfect Playback" Dictation ☐
Please arrange a no-obligation demonstration in my office ☐
Please tell me the location of my nearest Stenocord dealer ☐

NAME_____

ADDRESS_____

CITY_____STATE_____

See Stenocord at the National Business Show (New York City's Coliseum, October 20-24) — Booth #108-AB.

15

1958

At the request of President Eisenhower, 1,200 national leaders gather in Washington to voice support for the foreign aid plan deemed to be vital to defense.

Among some of the dignitaries in attendance are Secretary of State John Foster Dulles *(left)*, Adlai Stevenson and former president Harry S. Truman all of whom are putting national security above politics.

Secretary of State John Foster Dulles calls Harold Macmillan's attention to the portrait of Winston Churchill painted by Ike.

Truman addresses the assembled leaders.

In his address, President Eisenhower criticizes those who are not supporting his program:

Summit Talks Held At Walter Reed General

"What the ostrich-like opponents to mutual security seem to be saying is this: billions for armaments but not one cent for peace..."

Seated left to right, Foreign Secretary Lloyd, President Eisenhower, Mr. Macmillan and Mr. Dulles all agree in principles and broad policy on the problems with Germany and end the session "with fine results..."

NATIONAL NAVAL MEDICAL CENTER

16

RUSSIA BEGINS TO FULFILL WIDELY PUBLICIZED PLEDGE TO WITHDRAW 41,000 TROOPS FROM EAST GERMANY

A large German crowd gathers to watch the festivities as the first 500 troops prepare to leave.

Holding bouquets given them by German children, the Russian soldiers wave good-bye.

ELECTIONS HELD IN RUSSIA FOR SOVIET PARLIAMENT

Communist party boss Nikita Khrushchev *(above)*, casting his ballot and despite not getting 100% of the vote he is supreme ruler of all the U.S.S.R. as shown by the resignation of Premiere Bulganin *(below)* in Khrushchev's favor.

Khrushchev becomes the first man since Stalin to be both Premiere and Party Boss.

WHAT A YEAR IT WAS!

United Arab Republic Is Formed

A historic alliance takes place as Egypt's Nasser and Syria's President sign pact creating the United Arab Republic.

The new state numbers 30 million, largest in the Mideast, and Nasser invites all Arab states to join.

The motorcade is met with much enthusiasm as it moves through the streets of Cairo.

The effect on the precarious balance in the Middle East is unknown and the rest of the world, especially America, Russia and Israel, remain cautiously quiet as they try to anticipate the impact of this alliance.

1958

President Eisenhower dispatches 14,000 troops into Lebanon invoking the Eisenhower Doctrine.

President Eisenhower establishes the National Aeronautics and Space Administration (NASA) to direct nonmilitary space activities.

PRESIDENT EISENHOWER APPOINTS POTTER STEWART TO THE SUPREME COURT.

In an effort to bolster the sagging economy in the worst economic recession since World War II, Ike signs $1.8 million Emergency Housing Bill and allocates $10 billion for construction projects and extended unemployment benefits.

U.S. ARMY FORMS THE STRATEGIC ARMY CORPS COMPRISED OF 150,000 SPECIAL TROOPS TRAINED TO INTERVENE IN LIMITED WAR SITUATIONS WORLDWIDE.

U.S. EMBARGOES ARMS SHIPMENTS TO CUBA.

SENATOR JOHN F. KENNEDY RE-ELECTED SENATOR FROM MASSACHUSETTS AS DEMOCRATS TAKE CONTROL OF CONGRESS.

SENATE MAJORITY LEADER:
LYNDON B. JOHNSON

SPEAKER OF THE HOUSE:
SAM RAYBURN

DEMOCRATS CONSIDER SENATOR JOHN F. KENNEDY THE STRONGEST PRESIDENTIAL CANDIDATE TO OPPOSE VICE PRESIDENT RICHARD NIXON.

The House of Representatives passes and sends a bill to the White House providing a **$25,000** yearly pension to former U.S. Presidents and **$10,000** to their widows.

WEST GERMAN PRESIDENT THEODOR HEUSS ARRIVES IN WASHINGTON ON FIRST OFFICIAL VISIT BY A GERMAN CHIEF OF STATE.

Dynamite Destroys Tennessee's Clinton High School Integrated In 1956.

Tensions grow in the U.S. as desegregation of Southern schools is attempted. Key Negro* leaders including 29-year old Baptist Minister Martin Luther King, Jr., and Roy Wilkins meet with the President who makes no commitments to them.

Arkansas Governor Orval Faubus wins third term – defies Supreme Court by closing schools in Little Rock, later reopening them as private segregated schools.

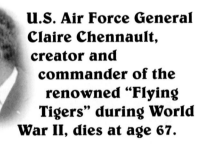

Martin Luther King, Jr.,
stabbed with steel letter opener by Negro woman as he autographs copies of his book "STRIDE TOWARD FREEDOM: THE MONTGOMERY STORY."

Martin Luther King, Jr., arrested in Alabama for loitering and refusing to obey the police.

"Evasive Schemes" To Avoid School Integration Banned By Supreme Court.

Civil rights activist Rev. Fred Shuttleworth escapes injury as bomb explodes outside his church.

NELSON A. ROCKEFELLER ELECTED GOVERNOR OF NEW YORK.

A PERMANENT SMALL BUSINESS ADMINISTRATION IS CREATED.

* Negro was the commonly used term in 1958 and is used throughout this book.

ALASKA Becomes 49th State Shifting The Geographic Center Of The Country.

White House announces that Alaska will be proclaimed the 49th State of the Union by President Eisenhower on January 3, 1959.

THE U.S. CIVIL SERVICE COMMISSION CELEBRATES ITS 75TH ANNIVERSARY.

DEPARTURES:

U.S. Air Force General Claire Chennault, creator and commander of the renowned "Flying Tigers" during World War II, dies at age 67.

U.S. Air Force Officer James H. Doolittle, Jr. dies at age 56.

Iraq's King Faisal II, head of the Arab Federation uniting Iraq and his cousin King Hussein's country of Jordan, is killed by revolutionaries in Baghdad at the young age of 23.

Herbert O. Yardley, Japanese code-breaking father of cryptography, dies at age 69.

Ruth Jones checks telephone handsets at our Indianapolis Works.

TELEPHONE HANDSET TAKES FINAL EXAM

This "mechanical voice" testing machine gives the last of dozens of tests to a telephone handset. When combined with the rest of the telephone it will be turned over to a Bell telephone company and put to work . . . to serve you long and faithfully.

High quality is built into all the products Western Electric makes . . . the telephone itself, wire and cable, huge dial switching systems . . . yet we thoroughly test everything before it goes to the Bell telephone companies.

Why? Because all must stand ready to work together instantly and perfectly if you are to enjoy dependable telephone service.

Making telephone equipment that won't let you down . . . that's Western Electric's main job as manufacturing and supply unit of the Bell System.

Western Electric manufacturing and supply unit of the Bell System

Elvis Presley is about to change his Rock & Roll beat to the tempo of *Hup 1, 2, 3* as he reports for his induction into the U.S. Army.

Private Presley reports to Camp Chaffee in Arkansas to begin his two-year hitch courtesy of local draft board #86 in Memphis.

Elvis GOES TO THE ARMY

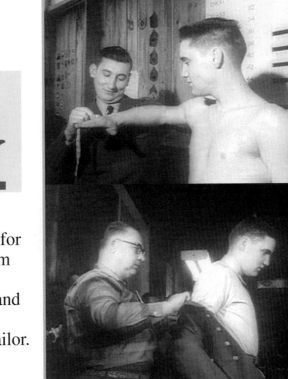

Elvis is measured for his uniform and gets a helping hand from a friendly tailor.

The King of Rock & Roll, whose earnings will slide from over $100,000 a month to a mere $83.20, will soon be keeping time to the sound of bugle calls.

AMERICA'S YOUNG VIRTUOSO
Van Cliburn
WINS PRESTIGIOUS MOSCOW COMPETITION

23-year old Van Cliburn, of Texas, is one of the few Americans to get to the finals of the Tchaikovsky piano competition, one of the world's toughest and most prestige-filled events for ambitious virtuosi.

Van Cliburn's passionate rendition of *"Rachmaninoff's Piano Concerto No. 3"* is the highlight of the competition.

History is made at the keyboards and overnight this American born and American trained pianist is catapulted into the ranks of the masters. Van Cliburn becomes the toast of Muscovites who nickname him *"Malchik"* or *"Little Boy."*

HOLLYWOOD IMPRESARIO MIKE TODD KILLED IN PLANE CRASH

Miss Taylor is in a state of collapse on hearing of the tragedy.

Mike Todd had made and lost several fortunes. Less than 10 years ago he was bankrupt but at his untimely death at the age of 49 years, he was the producer of "Around The World In 80 Days" and happily married to one of Hollywood's reigning beauties.

Mike Todd pictured here on a recent visit to Spain with his beautiful wife, Elizabeth Taylor.

Dorothy Does the Ball

Darling
Dorothy Dolliver
Is This Year's Queen Of The New York Press Photographer's Ball

WHAT A YEAR IT WAS!

MIDSEASON SENSATION . . . NEW WINDSOR DARTLINE

It's all Chrysler and you'll like the price!

You want to just stand back and drink in this brilliant new Chrysler with its glistening new chromework and sparkling new colors.

But the real excitement comes when you get in and get going. The moment your hands touch the wheel you sense that this car wasn't made to sit still. You touch a button and in seconds you're effortlessly out on the open road.

As it irons out the rough spots, you know why Chrysler pioneered Torsion-Aire Ride. Under your foot you feel a reservoir of power, thanks to Chrysler's TorqueFlite transmission.

The stopping power of its sure-footed Total-Contact Brakes is more than a match for Chrysler's incredible go power. Styled for attraction, engineered for action—this Chrysler is *all* car. It's a car you drive because you want to, not just because you have to.

And it's never been so easy to step up to Chrysler. You can own the magnificent new Chrysler Windsor *Dartline* for only a few dollars a month more than most small cars!

See it—price it—at your Chrysler dealer today. Chrysler's a thrill you shouldn't miss.

EXTRA!

AMAZING NEW

auto-pilot

A Chrysler Engineering Exclusive that patrols your speed . . . conserves gas . . . lets you cruise accelerator-free.

SEE AND DRIVE **THE MIGHTY CHRYSLER DART**LINE

THE HARVARD LAMPOON AWARDS

And The Dubious Honors Go To

ROCK HUDSON
Worst Actor

KIM NOVAK
Worst Actress

PAT BOONE
Most Inauspicious Male Debut

SUZY PARKER
Most Inauspicious Female Debut

ELEANOR ROOSEVELT

Tops The "Most Admired Woman" List For The 11th Year With

QUEEN ELIZABETH

Coming In Second.

A DRESSLESS OCCASION

Naked on the spacious lawns and gardens of the Duke of Bedford's Woburn Abbey for the sixth annual "World Congress" more than a thousand nudists from 40 countries gather while the Duke is in Canada discussing the preservation of Anglo-Saxon values.

NOBEL PEACE PRIZE

Georges Pire, Belgium, Father of the Dominican Order.

OH FOR THE GOOD OLD DAYS

When asked why he doesn't like the 20th Century, Pulitzer Prize winning author MacKinlay Kantor summarized by saying he dislikes ball-point pens, television and Zsa Zsa Gabor.

A FINAL STOMP AT THE SAVOY

An auction is held at Harlem's famed Savoy Ballroom, soon to be replaced by a housing project, and the Steinway piano whose keys were tickled by Fats Waller, Duke Ellington and Count Basie sells for $450.

1958

JORDAN'S 23-YEAR OLD KING HUSSEIN BECOMES THE WORLD'S NUMBER ONE TARGET FOR ASSASSINATION SINCE THE MURDER OF HIS COUSIN, FAISAL OF IRAQ.

THE EGYPTIAN GOVERNMENT ANNOUNCES THAT FORMER KING FAROUK AND HIS FAMILY ARE BEING STRIPPED OF THEIR CITIZENSHIP.

Britain's Prince Philip collides with a London taxi as he is being driven to make a speech before the British Automobile Association on the subject of safe driving. His opening remark:

"One should think about the prevention of accidents..."

CELEBRATING WITH A BANG

PRINCESS MARGRETHE, ELDEST DAUGHTER OF KING FREDERICK AND QUEEN INGRID OF COPENHAGEN, CELEBRATES HER 18TH BIRTHDAY WITH A 21-GUN SALUTE AND OFFICIALLY ASSUMES HER DUTIES AS HEIR-PRESUMPTIVE TO DANISH THRONE.

I SAY, DID YOU CALL ME FATTY?

Prince Charles, now the new Prince of Wales, punches a teammate in the nose during a soccer game after his schoolmate called him "fatty" when Charles accidentally stepped on his foot.

Britain's Princess Margaret celebrates her 28th birthday with her family at Balmoral Castle in Scotland.

GIRL'S NIGHT OUT

The first of its kind to be held since World War II, eleven unmarried Princesses are among the 7,000 guests who attend King Baudouin of Belgium's Royal Court Ball honoring the Brussels World's Fair.

In what was decreed the last of this particular form of privileged Coming Out Parties, 480 Debutantes are greeted by Queen Elizabeth and Prince Philip at Buckingham Palace. In the future, young Debs will have to co-mingle at Royal Garden parties with people from all strata of society.

WINNERS OF BRUSSELS WORLD'S FAIR POPULARITY CONTEST

Favorite American Actress	Kim Novak
Favorite Statesman	Abraham Lincoln
Favorite Musician	Louis Armstrong
Most Important Immigrant To The United States	Albert Einstein

WILL THE APPLES FALL FAR FROM THE TREES?

Child star Shirley Temple Black's three children hired as extras in a new children's TV series so they can see how mom earns her living.

LLOYD'S OF LONDON ISSUES SPECIAL LIBEL INSURANCE ON MARY ASTOR'S TELL-ALL AUTOBIOGRAPHY.

Marilyn Monroe's Playwright Husband Arthur Miller Acquitted Of Contempt Of Congress For Refusing To Name Communists.

Marilyn Monroe is quoted as saying that it isn't necessary for a man to continue courting his wife after they marry and that if she wants flowers she should buy them herself if he's too busy working.

Groucho Marx turns down $1,000 to play the drunken jailer in the Metropolitan Opera's production of "Die Fledermaus" saying that he makes that much just for walking his dog.

At an interview in Hollywood Groucho Marx says that no one thing guarantees a laugh and that Sid Caesar, Bob Hope and Jackie Gleason should be knighted because their brand of comedy is almost universally funny.

SINGING FOR YOUR SUPPER AND PAYING FOR IT TOO

$23.81 is the price Mr. and Mrs. Harry S. Truman, Frank Sinatra and Noel Coward each pay for admission to Princess Grace and Prince Rainier's Sing-Along Charity Benefit for the U.N. Children's Fund held in their castle.

Brigitte
A BRIG-ITTE NOT TOO FAR

New sex symbol Brigitte Bardot says she is just a passing fancy and will be forgotten in three years.

Elvis Presley Is Sent To West Germany By The Army In A Non-Musical Role As A Truck Driver.

Elvis

ELVIS PRESLEY OVERWHELMED WITH GRIEF ON THE DEATH OF HIS BELOVED MOTHER GLADYS.

Princess Grace

Prince Rainier demands the seduction scene be cut from Francoise Sagan's first ballet "BROKEN DATE" being directed by Roger Vadim or he and Princess Grace would not attend the performance.

Queen Elizabeth Opens 300th Session Of Parliament

QUEEN ELIZABETH accompanied by the Duke of Edinburgh enters the Hall of Parliament for the opening session never before filmed or seen by the public. In a ceremony rich in color and tradition, the Queen

wears the ruby-studded imperial crown and the robe of Parliament.

IN HER ADDRESS the Queen says that for the first time this ceremony is being watched by millions of her subjects and people in other lands. Besides the pageantry and symbols, she hopes that "...In their hearts they would respond to the spirit of hope and purpose which inspires our Parliamentary tradition."

Iran's Ex-Queen Soraya, divorced by the Shah because of her failure to provide him with an heir to the throne, arrives in New York aboard the Constitution.

Queen Soraya's story stirred sympathy and debate around the world but at this point she declines any comments about her future.

WHAT A YEAR IT WAS!

Queen Elizabeth and her consort Phillip arrive on the Royal Yacht in Amsterdam Harbor for the first Royal visit by any reigning British Monarch to the Netherlands.

Queen Wilhelmina greets Queen Elizabeth in a Queenly welcome.

Queen Elizabeth kisses the welcoming Princess Beatrix.

This is an occasion that calls for the utmost of ceremony especially in Holland with its fondness for royalty.

This historic joint appearance by the two Queens meets with great enthusiasm by the throngs of people lined up to witness this occasion.

1958

Robert Frost Takes Over As Consultant Of Poetry At The Library Of Congress.

THE WORLD'S MOST POPULAR CHARMING MEN

Vittorio De Sica
Sir Edmund Hillary
Leonard Bernstein
Peter Lawford
Senator John Kennedy
Eric Sevareid

Anthony Nutting
James Reston
Lew Hoad
Marlon Brando
William Humphrey
Yul Brynner
Cesare Siepi
William Holden

It's A Man's World, Isn't It?

Author Pearl S. Buck confesses that she wrote the best selling novels "The Townsman" and "The Long Love" under the nom de plume John Sedges … "because men have fewer handicaps in our society than women have in writing as well as in other professions…"

The World's Most Distinguished Living Poet T.S. Eliot Celebrates His 70th Birthday With His New 31-Year Old Bride.

14-year old Cheryl Crane, daughter of Hollywood movie star Lana Turner, fatally stabs her mother's boyfriend, Johnny Stompanato in defense of her mother.

Aga Khan IV New Head Of Ismaili Moslems.

Angelo Giuseppe Roncalli Elected 262nd Pope And Becomes John XXIII.

DOOM & GLOOM

In a speech presented to British pacifists gathering in London's Central Hall, Nobel Prize winner Bertrand Russell warns of dire consequences if the H-bomb is not banned predicting that if the world continues on its present destructive path there is a 50-50 chance that human beings will survive beyond the next 40 years.

THE WAY TO THIS MAN'S HEART

SIR WINSTON AND LADY CHURCHILL CELEBRATE THEIR GOLDEN ANNIVERSARY. MRS. CHURCHILL'S KEY TO KEEPING HIM HAPPY? FEED HIM WELL.

WINSTON CHURCHILL'S ONE-MAN ART SHOW OPENS IN NELSON GALLERY IN KANSAS CITY TO A RECORD CROWD AND GLOWING REACTION.

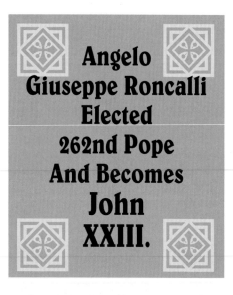

American Singer PAUL ROBESON Is Made Honorary Professor At The Moscow State Conservatory Of Music.

WHAT A YEAR IT WAS!

THE TEN MOST POPULAR HEROES

Abraham Lincoln

Albert Schweitzer

Thomas Jefferson

Socrates

Julius Caesar

Albert Einstein

William Shakespeare

St. Francis of Assisi

Franklin D. Roosevelt

Sir Winston Churchill

Quiz Show Rigging Uncovered
With Charles Van Doren and Herbert Stemple Leading The List Of Guilty Contestants.

HELL NO, WE WON'T GO Members of the "Ban The Bomb" organization arrested for refusing to take shelter during a civil defense alert in New York City.

Comedian Red Skelton almost succumbs to severe asthmatic attack but has life breathed back into him by the fire department.

A Warrant Is Issued In New York City For The Arrest Of Judy Garland For Income Tax Evasion.

SOME LIKE IT RED Grandma Moses' friend, 79-year old Leo Schutzman denies giving the 98-year old painter a red negligee. Turns out it was really a quilted robe.

Primitive painter Grandma Moses celebrates her 98th birthday In Eagle Bridge, New York where, despite her failing health, she continues to paint.

Academy Award Winning Monocled Actor Charles Coburn Celebrates His 81st Birthday.

Don McNeill Celebrates his 25th Year as host of the "Breakfast Club" aired on ABC Radio.

A REALLY GOOD "SHEW"
Ed Sullivan completes his 10th year on television.

STAY HOME UGLY AMERICAN
Former President of General Electric Charles E. Wilson urges American tourists to leave their casual clothes at home when they travel abroad. Men should not be caught dead going into a cathedral in shirt sleeves while women must not even think about wearing slacks to church.

Coupling

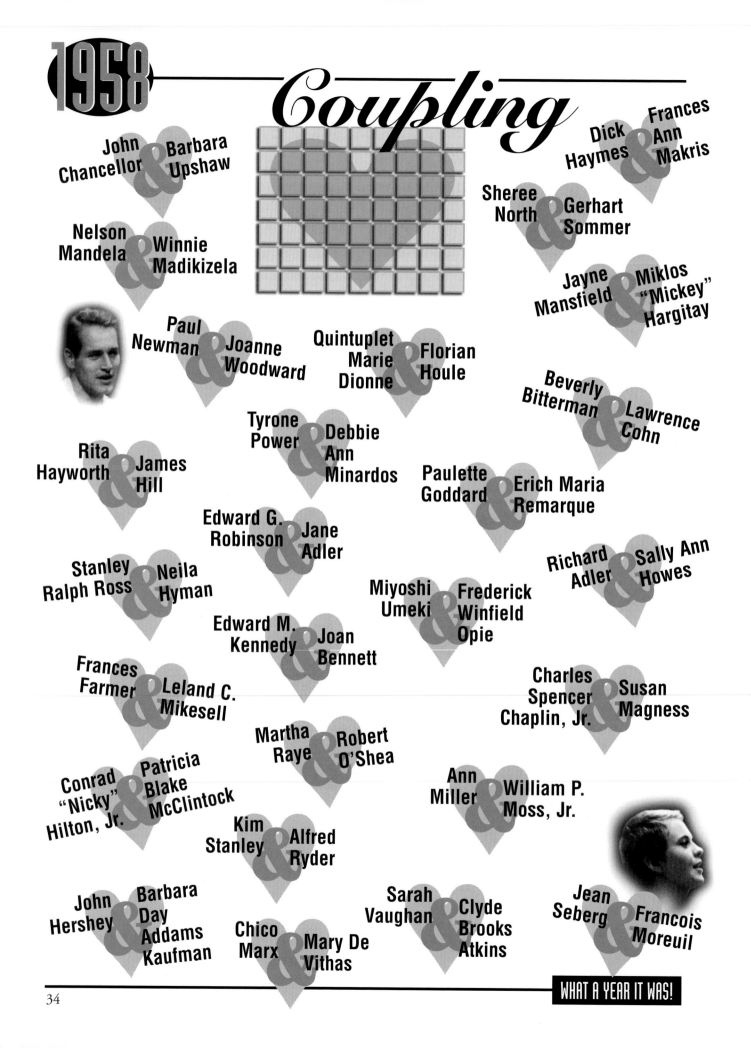

John Chancellor & Barbara Upshaw

Dick Haymes & Frances Ann Makris

Nelson Mandela & Winnie Madikizela

Sheree North & Gerhart Sommer

Paul Newman & Joanne Woodward

Jayne Mansfield & Miklos "Mickey" Hargitay

Quintuplet Marie Dionne & Florian Houle

Beverly Bitterman & Lawrence Cohn

Tyrone Power & Debbie Ann Minardos

Rita Hayworth & James Hill

Paulette Goddard & Erich Maria Remarque

Edward G. Robinson & Jane Adler

Stanley Ralph Ross & Neila Hyman

Richard Adler & Sally Ann Howes

Miyoshi Umeki & Frederick Winfield Opie

Edward M. Kennedy & Joan Bennett

Frances Farmer & Leland C. Mikesell

Charles Spencer Chaplin, Jr. & Susan Magness

Martha Raye & Robert O'Shea

Conrad "Nicky" Hilton, Jr. & Patricia Blake McClintock

Ann Miller & William P. Moss, Jr.

Kim Stanley & Alfred Ryder

John Hershey & Barbara Day Addams Kaufman

Sarah Vaughan & Clyde Brooks Atkins

Jean Seberg & Francois Moreuil

Chico Marx & Mary De Vithas

"America's Sweethearts"

Eddie Fisher and Debbie Reynolds break up as Elizabeth Taylor declares Eddie never really loved Debbie.

Uncoupling

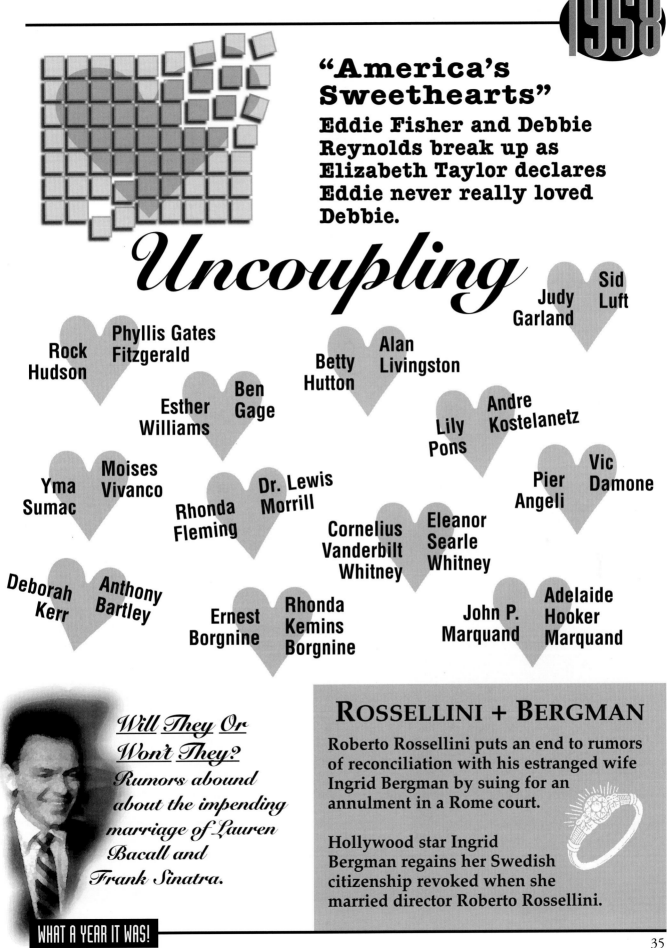

Judy Garland — Sid Luft

Rock Hudson — Phyllis Gates Fitzgerald

Betty Hutton — Alan Livingston

Esther Williams — Ben Gage

Lily Pons — Andre Kostelanetz

Yma Sumac — Moises Vivanco

Rhonda Fleming — Dr. Lewis Morrill

Pier Angeli — Vic Damone

Cornelius Vanderbilt Whitney — Eleanor Searle Whitney

Deborah Kerr — Anthony Bartley

Ernest Borgnine — Rhonda Kemins Borgnine

John P. Marquand — Adelaide Hooker Marquand

Will They Or Won't They?

Rumors abound about the impending marriage of Lauren Bacall and Frank Sinatra.

ROSSELLINI + BERGMAN

Roberto Rossellini puts an end to rumors of reconciliation with his estranged wife Ingrid Bergman by suing for an annulment in a Rome court.

Hollywood star Ingrid Bergman regains her Swedish citizenship revoked when she married director Roberto Rossellini.

WHAT A YEAR IT WAS!

IKE MEETS THE PRESS

Says He Feels Fine, And Lauds Dulles

Ike is asked about the state of his health.

Ike's reply to the question is that despite some serious illnesses he is feeling "very well indeed" and that "...if the sun was shining at this moment, I would be on the golf course..."

When asked about the growing criticism of Secretary of State Dulles both here and abroad and an alleged report that said Mr. Dulles had submitted a letter of resignation which the President rejected, Eisenhower replies:

Ike: "Have you seen that report or have you written it yourself?"

Reporter: "No sir. It was in the newspaper."

Ike: "Then I would say I would classify it as trash. The last person I would want to see resign is Mr. Dulles..."

IRON DEFICIENCY ANEMIA CURED THE HARD WAY

Convicted spy Jacob Sobel *(above)* attempts suicide before scheduled appearance before the federal grand jury by swallowing over a pound of hardware including nuts, bolts and rivets.

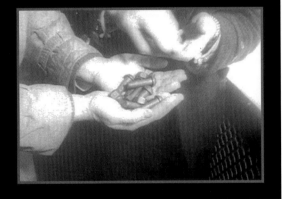

Jimmy Doolittle Remembered

Replica of the B-25 bomber flown by World War II flying ace Jimmy Doolittle on his historic raid on Tokyo less than a year after Pearl Harbor, taxis down a Las Vegas highway on its way to the Tropicana Hotel for a reunion of the Tokyo Raiders.

Survivors of that historic mission gather for ceremonies where the plane is formally presented to the Air Museum in Dayton, Ohio.

Celebrating its 15th anniversary in Valley Forge, the Freedom Foundation presents former president Herbert Hoover with its highest honor, the George Washington award, "...For outstanding achievements in bringing about a better understanding of the American way of life..."

The plane will serve as a tangible memorial of an achievement that crowned the pioneering career of Jimmy Doolittle, one of America's greatest airmen.

1958

Radio And TV Commentator **EDWARD R. MURROW** Turns Down Senate Bid Offered To Him By New York's Liberal Party.

A car carrying Janet Leigh, Tony Curtis and Dean Martin is rear-ended by a man who mistakes Miss Leigh for his wife.

Comedian Buddy Hackett pays $64,000 for spanish-style mansion in Fort Lee, New Jersey formerly owned by gangster Albert Anastasia.

GYPSY ROSE LEE faints from the heat during the opening of "Happy Hunting" at the Westbury Music Fair.

Actress Suzy Parker is discharged from the hospital for special surgery where she has been recovering from a fatal car accident that killed her father.

EDWARD M. KENNEDY, ATTENDING THE UNIVERSITY OF VIRGINIA LAW SCHOOL, ENGAGED TO JOAN BENNETT, A SENIOR AT MANHATTANVILLE COLLEGE.

CAUGHT IN THE WEB... OR JUST THE VOWS, MA'AM
Jack Webb marries Jackie Loughery, Miss America 1952.

84-Year Old Former President Hoover Donates His $25,000 Pension To Charities.

Angry over plans to construct a new superhighway along the ocean front of Olympic National Park, U.S. Supreme Court Justice William O. Douglas leads 70 friends on a 22-mile protest march.

FORMER PRESIDENT HARRY TRUMAN, LYNDON JOHNSON AND HOUSE SPEAKER SAM RAYBURN AMONG POLITICAL FIGURES WHO GATHER TO CELEBRATE FORMER VICE PRESIDENT JOHN NANCE GARNER'S 90TH BIRTHDAY.

David Sarnoff, Chairman of the Radio Corp. of America, receives Honorary High School Diploma from New York's Stuyvesant High School 52 years after he graduated from the 8th grade, the end of his formal schooling.

THE CHILDREN, THE CHILDREN, WE CAN'T FORGET THE CHILDREN.
The "Save The Children Award" is presented to Countess Mountbatten, wife of Earl Louis Mountbatten of Burma.

Wounded three times in Korea, U.S. Army Sergeant David W. Martin finds himself facing deportation proceedings on discovery he is an illegal alien from Poland.

WHAT A YEAR IT WAS!

WITHOUT SUB-TITLES
Beautiful silent film stars Dorothy and Lillian Gish agree to appear on Broadway together in "The Children's Playhouse."

THEY DIDN'T KNOW WHAT HIT THEM
Former Heavyweight Champion Of The World JERSEY JOE WALCOTT, Now A Special Investigator For The Camden Juvenile Bureau, K.O.'s Five Teenagers Who Were Attacking A Policeman.

Harvard's Hasty Pudding Institute Of 1770 WOMAN OF THE YEAR Award Presented To Katharine Hepburn.

THE MALIBU RUM & COCA COLA PARTY
Sarah Churchill arrested in her Malibu Beach house after a nasty confrontation with a telephone operator followed by a verbal assault on police sent to investigate the offended operator's complaint.

LABELLING HOLLYWOOD AS BEING SEX OBSESSED WITH WOMEN WITH NO RESPECT FOR THEIR DIGNITY, OLIVIA DE HAVILLAND REVEALS THAT A COMBINATION OF LIVING IN FRANCE WITH HER HUSBAND PIERRE GALANTE AND THE PRACTICE OF YOGA IS RESPONSIBLE FOR HER PEACEFUL, HAPPY LIFE.

PASSINGS

12-Year old **Timothy Getty**, son of Jean Paul Getty, dies of a heart ailment in New York.

Winner of the first Pulitzer Prize for reporting, New York World journalist and editor **Herbert Swope**, known for his "scoops," dies at age 76.

A SPIT BALL
On being booed by Kansas City fans, Boston Red Sox slugger Ted Williams loses his temper and spits at the crowd resulting in a $250 fine.

TEA & "THE MAN IN THE MOON IS A LADY"
Falling attendance at the Wednesday matinee performances of "Auntie Mame" prompted producer David Pelham to make an announcement that the customary tea during intermission will be served by members of the cast including Bea Lillie who plays the starring role. Results? A packed house for the next matinee.

WHAT? WEAR THIS OLD ROBE?
Upset that the red and ermine trimmed robes and 3-cornered hats worn by the Lords are terribly unfeminine, the First Women appointed to the British House of Lords are given a concession that allows them to wear gold-lace rosettes and sequins on their hats.

Javier Pereira, purported to be the world's oldest living man, dies at age 168 in a small South American town.

THE 50TH ANNUAL CONVENTION OF THE HOBOES OF AMERICA IS HELD AT CINCINNATI'S NETHERLANDS HILTON HOTEL.

Swing into Spring ...with a Texaco Safe-T Check-up

Special BENNY GOODMAN
"Swing into Spring" Record Album
$1.29 VALUE **Only 50¢**
SEE YOUR TEXACO DEALER
— for your record album coupon

Here's how your Texaco Dealer gets you set for Spring, saves you money, and helps to assure safer driving for your family.

1. He Safe-T checks and services your lights, tires, radiator, battery, brake fluid, and other potential trouble spots! **2.** He leaves nothing to chance, lubricates by chart, and gives you a record of work done. **3.** He cushions the chassis with Marfak, for quieter riding, easier handling, greater comfort. **4.** Services your automatic transmission — uses Texamatic Fluid. **5.** And — to protect your engine, Havoline Special 10W-30 the all-temperature motor oil. This is the revolutionary new motor oil that thinks for itself — to save you thinking about seasonal grades! **6.** Finally, your Texaco Dealer fills 'er up with top octane Texaco Sky Chief Su-preme with Petrox . . . or lively-powered, regular-price Texaco Fire Chief gasoline. Both are 100% Climate-Controlled!

THE TEXAS COMPANY

TEXACO
DEALERS in all 48 states
Texaco Products are also distributed in Canada, Latin America, and Africa

HUMAN INTEREST

HULA-HOOP MADNESS

Spins Itself Across The Ocean To Europe And Africa

LONDON

BELGIUM

WEST GERMANY

FRENCH BALLET ACADEMY

**and where it all began...
in the good old
U.S. of A.**

Samsonite folding tables and chairs – big gifts with little price tags

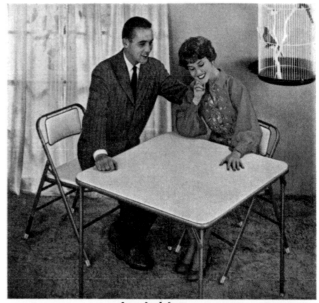

for mothers . . . table, $12.95; chair, $7.95

for brides . . . table, $14.95; chair, $8.95

birthdays . . . table, $17.95; chair, $9.95; armchair, $17.95

anniversaries . . . table, $8.95; chair, $7.95

Here are ideal gifts – Samsonite Folding Tables and Chairs—perfect for *any* occasion! Samsonite chairs give you extra seating space in a twinkling—are a snap to store. Versatile Samsonite tables serve as desks, work areas, even dining tables! And Samsonite's beauty *lasts!* The smart vinyl surfaces wipe clean with a damp cloth . . . the satin-smooth baked enamel finish can't snag stockings. Samsonite folding furniture flicks open and closed at a touch, stores in little space. Choose it for *every* gift occasion! In a choice of colors.

For mothers—the PlastiShield table (textured vinyl permanently sealed to metal) can't burn, scratch, or stain. Green with grey frame, matching chair.

For brides—"King-Size" table, in antique white and bronze, has a top with over 200 square inches extra. Matching Futura chair.

For birthdays—the oval table makes a charming and unusual dining table. In tombola brown. Matching chair and armchair.

For anniversaries — vinyl top folding table in metallic flame and black. A magnificent gift at a modest price. Matching chair.

Shwayder Bros., Inc., Folding Furniture Division, Detroit 29, Michigan. Also manufacturers of Samsonite Streamlite and Ultralite Luggage, and Samsonite Classroom Furniture. Available in Canada through Samsonite of Canada, Ltd., Stratford, Ontario, at slightly higher prices. © 1958

MORE HULA-HOOP MADNESS

THE WINNERS
NYC: Terri Seskin, 10
4,010 rotations in 45 minutes
CHICAGO: James McDonald, 9
21,000 spins in 3 hours,
35 minutes

THE LOSERS
AKRON: Mrs. Dana Cramer, 58
fractured hip
MICHIGAN: Harold Dukes, 25
dislocated a vertebra

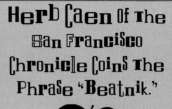

Herb Caen Of The San Francisco Chronicle Coins The Phrase "Beatnik."

The "Beatnik" Movement Begins In California And Spreads Throughout The United States And Europe.

IN SEARCH OF THE SWEETEST OF THE SWEET

Celebrating National Retail Bakers Week, the Associated Retail Bakers of America sponsor a "Little Miss Muffin" contest with the Little Muffin contestants flown in to the National Convention in New York. And the winning Muffin is... Susan Gratzel, 7, Teaneck, New Jersey.

COULD YOU REPEAT WHAT YOU SAID DEAR?

About 11% Of The World's Children Write With Their Left Hand.

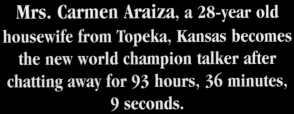

Mrs. Carmen Araiza, a 28-year old housewife from Topeka, Kansas becomes the new world champion talker after chatting away for 93 hours, 36 minutes, 9 seconds.

NATHAN LEOPOLD, Who Together With RICHARD LOEB, Kidnapped And Murdered Bobby Franks In 1924, Is Paroled After Serving A 34-Year Jail Term.

CHARLES STARKWEATHER, A 19-Year Old Trash Collector, Along With His 14-Year Old Girlfriend, CARIL FUGATE, Are Arrested For The Deaths Of Ten People Including Her Mother, Step-Father and Step-Sister.

THE STRONG SILENT TYPE

VITO GENOVESE, 60-Year Old Mafia Mastermind In The United States, Takes The Fifth Amendment 150 Times During His Appearance Before The Senate Rackets Investigating Committee.

NOW IF WE COULD JUST FIND AN AXE MURDERER

Using the same academic principles as medical schools where the students work on cadavers, a criminology professor at Oklahoma State University decides to give his students a hands-on experience by bringing in a prostitute as a lecturer followed by a pickpocket.

FIRST CLASS Postage Is Raised From $.03 to $.04 Per Ounce. Airmail Goes From $.06 To $.07.

POSTMASTER General Arthur Summerfield Announces That If Your Dog Bites A Mailman, You'll Have To Fetch Your Own Mail.

BUT YOUR HONOR, I OBSERVE THE SABBATH ON SATURDAY

New Jersey Passes Legislation Making It Illegal To Do Business On Sundays.

NEW YORK MAKES JAYWALKING ILLEGAL

Car Manufacturers Now Required To Affix A Price Tag To New Cars Under The Automotive Information Disclosure Act.

PRESIDENT EISENHOWER

Approves New Design For Reverse Side Of The Lincoln Penny.

BERNARD GOLDFINE, New England Industrialist, Admits To Handing Out Christmas Checks To 33 White House Aides.

FORMER U.S. PRESIDENTS

Collect Their First Pension Of $25,000 Yearly Along With Office Space, Free Postage And A $50,000 Annual Staff Allowance.

PROCLAIMING THAT THE COMMUNIST PARTY IS "...A FUTILE AND IMPOTENT POLITICAL SECT," JOHN GATES, EDITOR OF THE DAILY WORKER QUITS AND PUBLISHING CEASES.

U.S. SUPREME COURT BANS PASSPORT DENIALS TO SUSPECTED COMMUNISTS.

IN DIRECT RESPONSE TO THE SOVIET'S LAUNCHING OF SPUTNIK, THE NATIONAL DEFENSE EDUCATIONAL ACT IS PASSED WHICH ALLOCATES FUNDS TO BE CONTROLLED AT THE STATE AND COMMUNITY LEVEL FOR THE SPECIFIC PURPOSE OF PROMOTING THE STUDY OF SCIENCE, MATHEMATICS AND FOREIGN LANGUAGES.

THE MOISEYEV TROUPE OF FOLK DANCERS, ONE OF RUSSIA'S GREAT CULTURAL ATTRACTIONS, ARRIVE FOR A TOUR OF THE U.S. AND CANADA.

U.S. AND RUSSIA AGREE TO EXPAND CULTURAL EXCHANGE ACTIVITIES.

Unemployment Reaches High Of Almost 5.2 Million In The U.S., Highest Since 1941.

Average Work Week:	39 Hours
U.S. Population:	172.8 Million
Average Family Income:	$6,000

JIMMY HOFFA takes over as president of the International Brotherhood Of Teamsters. U.S. Senate calls Hoffa boss of "hoodlum empire" but he eludes criminal conviction making the Teamsters one of the nation's most powerful labor unions.

UNITED PRESS And **INTERNATIONAL NEWS SERVICE** Merge Forming **U.P.I.**

THERE'S SPENDABLE INCOME IN THEM THERE PURSES

Newspaper editors recognize women's buying power and seek to revitalize the women's pages by concentrating more on socially significant articles than on gossipy society news.

The Atomic Energy Commission Cancels A Scheduled Nuclear Test After Los Angeles Mayor Norris Poulson Strongly Protests.

Anti-Nuclear Protesters From New York, Connecticut And Pennsylvania Picket In Front Of The United Nations Building And Present A Petition To UN Secretary Dag Hammarskjold Asking For UN Assistance In Banning Further Tests.

WHAT A YEAR IT WAS!

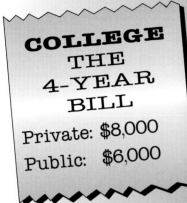

COLLEGE
THE
4-YEAR
BILL

Private: $8,000

Public: $6,000

SHOW ME THE WAY TO GO HOME, I'M TIRED AND I WANT MY MOMMY

At University of Cincinnati's counseling center, the most consistent problem is homesickness with nearly two-thirds of the worst cases being men due to the fact that they are taught to control rather than express their emotions.

With Stay-At-Home Study At An All-Time Peak, New Enrollments In Nation's Correspondence Schools Reaches Higher Number Than College Enrollments.

The U.S. Navy Is Without A Battleship For The First Time Since 1895 After Decommissioning The "Wisconsin."

The Civilian Ground Observer Corps. Is Discontinued By The United States Air Force.

The Army Secretly Tests LSD On U.S. Soldiers Without Disclosing The Dangerous Nature Of The Experiment.

The Remains Of Two Unknown Soldiers From World War II And Korea Enshrined At Arlington National Cemetery In The "Tomb Of The Unknown Soldier."

THE 1959 *Cadillac*

By appointment to the world's most discriminating motorists!

THE ELDORADO BIARRITZ

A NEW REALM OF MOTORING MAJESTY!

A single glance tells you, beyond any question, *that these are the newest and most magnificent Cadillac cars ever created.* Dazzling in their beauty, enchanting in their grace and elegance, and inspiring in their Fleetwood luxury and decor—they introduce a new realm of motoring majesty. And a single journey at the wheel will reveal still another unquestionable fact—*that these are the finest performing Cadillacs ever produced.* With a spectacular new engine, with a smoother, more responsive Hydra-Matic drive, and with improved qualities of ride and handling, they provide a totally new sense of mastery over time and distance. This brilliant new Cadillac beauty and this marvelous new Cadillac performance are offered in thirteen individual body styles. To see and to drive any of them is to acknowledge Cadillac a new measure of automotive supremacy. Your dealer invites you to do both at your first opportunity.

CADILLAC MOTOR CAR DIVISION • GENERAL MOTORS CORPORATION

THE SIXTY-TWO COUPE

60,000 PEOPLE GATHER

For Pontifical Mass In Lourdes, France To Celebrate Its 100th Anniversary Of Becoming A Holy Shrine.

10 Million People From All Over The World Come To The Shrine This Year To Seek Healing.

The Highest Churchmen From France Are In Attendance Along With Devout, Faithful Pilgrims.

DISCOVERY OF LONG-LOST RELATIVES

- **A** fossilized skeleton estimated to be 10,000,000 years old is discovered embedded in coal in an Italian mine.

- **E**arliest traces of man discovered in Tanganyika dating back about 400,000 years are dubbed "Chellean."

Cave of Pan, dating back to about 3500 B.C. and probably used in the worship of the pastoral god in ancient Greece, is discovered near Marathon, Greece.

THE PREHISTORIC PAINTED CAVE IN BORNEO IS DISCOVERED.

THE BRITISH MINISTRY OF WORKS BEGINS RESTORATION OF STONEHENGE NEAR AMESBURY, ENGLAND.

"B.C."-
A Caveman Comic Makes Its Strip Debut.

American Catholic Priests Richard Cushing And John O'Hara Become Cardinals.

Following A Huge Outcry From Jewish And Protestant Groups Over A Controversial Order By New York City's Hospital Commissioner Forbidding A Doctor At A City Hospital From Issuing A Prescription For Contraceptives For A Protestant Patient Whose Life Would Be Endangered By Another Pregnancy, The Board Of Hospitals Votes 8-2 To Overturn The Ban.

WHAT'LL WE DO FOR THE SEVENTH INNING STRETCH?
150,000 Jehovah's Witnesses gather in the Giantless Polo Grounds for their biggest convention in history.

ope Pius XII, who failed to condemn the Nazi extermination of Jews during World War II, dies at 82 and is succeeded by Pope John XXIII.

Passings

Travelogue inventor **Elias Burton Holmes**, who journeyed around the globe then shared his pictures and adventures with others, dies at the grand old age of 88.

Clyde Pangborn, pilot of the first nonstop flight over the Pacific Ocean, dies at age 61.

Inspiration for the play "The Rainmaker," **Charles M. Hatfield**, storm maker and drought breaker, dies at the age of 82.

American Foundation for the Blind founder, **Moses C. Migel**, who worked with Helen Keller and participated in making Braille a uniform system, dies at age 91.

The second to last surviving daughter of the "King of Siam," **Princess Napaporn Prapha Kromluang Dipsarat** dies at age 94.

THE U.S. HAS 47 MILLION TELEVISION SETS— TWO THIRDS OF THE WORLD'S T.V. SETS.

BEFORE IT BECAME A VAST WASTELAND
New York sponsors first educational television program.

Ford Foundation study reveals that students who had the advantage of class-room television did significantly better than students without television exposure.

FAMOUS BIRTH

Bill Watterson
(Calvin & Hobbes cartoonist)

Look at DAYSTROM dining furniture...
style and quality at a price you can afford now!

The really wonderful thing about Daystrom is the way it brightens any room...and your dining *mood*, too! Tables and chairs have a clean, uncluttered look. and make everyday meals more pleasant. And it's so *practical.* Daystromite® table tops have the beauty of rich wood *plus* the ability to resist scratches, stains — even cigarette burns! Wide selection of vinyl chair coverings in rich patterns and colors. Good looks and quality, too, at modest, realistic prices. Set above. *about $139.95.* Daystrom Serving Cart, *about $34.95.* At better dealers everywhere.

 "SO EASY TO CLEAN"...*Mrs. J. M. Bristow, Cleveland, Ohio* — Every inch of Daystrom whisks clean with a damp cloth or sponge. This 42-inch long table expands to 52 inches when leaf is added. Coloramic® black legs with self-leveling glides. Chairs in Gray "Sierra" pattern. *About $79.95.*

"WONDERFULLY COMFORTABLE CHAIRS!"... *Mrs. R. S. Farrington, Newton, Mass.* — Heavily-padded chairs covered in Tan "Nassau" vinyl surround this sturdy round table (shown with leaf) with a two-tone woodgrained top. Bronze leg finish with glistening brass appointments. *About $179.95.* *Prices slightly higher in West.*

 "I LOVE THE LINES"...*Mrs. D. C. Mitchell, San Francisco, California* — Compact Drop Leaf Table opens to a full 51 inches. Bronze legs swing out to keep it steady. "Driftwood" Daystromite® top. Tufflex-padded chairs in leather-like Green "Saddle" Vinyl. *About $89.95.*

 America dines best on  **Daystrom** FURNITURE OLEAN, N.Y.

Bridge To China

The first bridge to span the great Yangtze River in China is completed.

The ribbon is cut officially opening mile long bridge.

The crowd displays their jubilation at this remarkable engineering feat.

The first cars cross the bridge resulting in a colossal traffic jam.

53

Pecos County, Texas Is The Site Of The World's Deepest Oil Well Reaching Over 25,000 Feet.

World's Largest Oil Tanker Launched At Kure, Japan.

60,000-Ton Carrier "Independence" Christened In Brooklyn.

Canada and the United States participate in ceremonies kicking off power flow from St. Lawrence Station.

The 31-Story Pirelli Skyscraper Is Completed In Milan, Italy Becoming Europe's Tallest Steel And Concrete Building.

In Southern California, A $400,000,000 Redevelopment Project Called "Century City" Is Under Construction On The 20th Century Fox Lot.

BRIDGING THE GAPS

- **The Mackinac Bridge, world's longest suspension bridge, opens in St. Ignace, Michigan.**

- **Contracts are awarded for construction of a six-lane lower deck on the George Washington Bridge connecting New York and New Jersey.**

- **Bridging the Mississippi River, construction of the greater New Orleans Bridge is completed making it the longest cantilever-type in the United States.**

Italy Bans Legalized Prostitution For The First Time In 98 Years Becoming One Of The Last Of The Major Western Nations To Do So.

After Only Ten Days, The Brussels World's Fair Sees Its Millionth Visitor With A Total Of 41 Million Visitors Attending By Fair's End.

UNESCO Unveils Its New Home On Paris' Left Bank After Thirteen Years In Temporary Quarters.

Marcellin Cazas Receives The Legion Of Honor For Running The Best Literary Salon In Paris—Brasserie Lipp Opened In The 1870's.

Sweden Names Agda Rossel Permanent Head Of Its Delegation To The United Nations Becoming First Nation To Appoint A Woman To Such A Position.

HONEY, YOUR APRON IS THE ONE WITHOUT THE FLOWERS

In a report delivered to the U.N. Commission on the Status of Women, Secretary-General Dag Hammarskjold revealed a global trend for husbands to help with housework with the exception of French and Austrian men who refuse to wear an apron in any shape, manner or form.

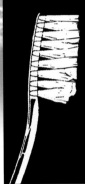

ONE, TWO, THREE SPIT

To celebrate "Keep Your Teeth Clean Week" 70,000 Japanese school children gather in Tokyo's National Stadium and brush their teeth in unison.

Queen Elizabeth II Names Her Son Prince Charles, Heir Apparent To The British Throne, Prince Of Wales.

2-Day Old Prince Albert Alexandre Louis Pierre, Son Of Prince Rainier And Princess Grace, Receives His Birth Certificate In Monaco Along With The Added Title Of Marquis de Baux.

Lord Chancellor Of The British House Of Lords Introduces First Women To Sit In The House Of Lords—Baroness Ravensdale, Dame Katharine Elliott, Mrs. Barbara Wootton Wright And Stella, Marchioness Of Reading. All Will Have Baroness Rank.

Richard Nixon Hosts Queen Elizabeth At A Thanksgiving Dinner Held In The U.S. Embassy In London.

Japan's Crown Prince Akihito Chooses Own Bride, A Commoner, Breaking Tradition.

WHAT A YEAR IT WAS!

1958

Pan American World Airways Begins Regular Transatlantic Service With A Boeing 707, The First U.S. Commercial Jet Airliner.

A National Airlines New York-Miami Flight Launches The First Regular Jet Passenger Service Within The United States.

Permission For The Regular Operation Of Jet Airliners From Idlewild, New York International Airport Granted To Port Of New York Authority.

20-Year Old Blond Israeli Yael Finkelstein Becomes World's First Female Airline Pilot.

Regular Helicopter Passenger Airport Service Is Established.

LET 'EM PAPER BAG IT!

Several airlines lodge protests over a Swiss airline's practice of serving sandwiches aboard the economy class flights on the grounds that the sandwiches are excessive according to the rules of the International Air Transport Association.

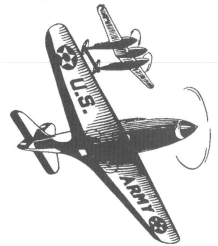

WOULD YOU FINISH THE DISHES DEAR... I HAVE TO GO FLY A PLANE

In her fourth victory as a pilot in the "Powder Puff Derby" flying a Beechcraft Bonanza, Mrs. Frances Bera and her co-pilot, Mrs. Evelyn Kelly, triumph in the all-woman transcontinental race from San Diego, California to Charleston, South Carolina at an average ground speed of 177.87439 M.P.H.

Helmeted And Smiling, Reporter Esther Clark Climbs Into The Passenger Seat Of An F100F Super Sabre, Takes Off From An Air Force Base Near Phoenix, Arizona And In A Half-Hour Flight She Soars 43,000 Feet Up And 400 Miles Out Over The Arizona Desert Becoming The First Newswoman To Travel At A Speed Of Nearly 1,000 Miles An Hour.

Flying A KC-135 Jet Tanker, General Curtis LeMay, Vice Chief Of Staff Of The U.S. Air Force, Makes Record-Breaking 7,100 Mile Flight From Tokyo, Japan To Andrews Air Force Base In 12 Hrs., 28 Min.

Two U.S. Jets Set Records: New York To London- 5 Hours, 56 Seconds; New York To Paris- 6 Hours, 16 Seconds.

The 22-Foot Twin-Outboard "Coronet Explorer" Makes Its Way Through The Waves From Copenhagen To New York In 10 Days, 16 Hours, 18 Minutes, Becoming The First Motorboat To Make An Atlantic Crossing.

Negro Women Demonstrate In South Africa Against The Use Of Identity Cards For Minorities.

Ruth Carol Taylor Becomes The First Negro Stewardess In The Nation As Mohawk Airlines Puts Her On The Ithaca-New York Run.

Negro Girl In Greensboro North Carolina Becomes First Negro To Graduate From A Former All-White School.

Harry Bridges, Left-Wing Leader Of The International Longshoremen's And Warehousemen's Union, Cracks Nevada's Anti-Miscegenation Law And Marries American-Born Japanese Woman.

A Klu Klux Klan Rally Held In South Carolina Broken Up By 500 Indians.

Atlanta Synagogue Destroyed By Bomb Blast. FBI Sent To Investigate. Five Men With Record Of Anti-Semitic Activity Indicted.

The John Birch Society Is Formed Under The Leadership Of Robert Welch.

WHAT A YEAR IT WAS!

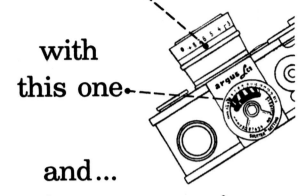

1958

Bing Crosby (54) and Kathy Grant (24) have their first child—Harry Lillis Crosby III.

Comedy Team Of **Charles Correll** *And* **Freeman Gosden,** *Known For 31 Years As* **Amos 'n' Andy,** *Celebrate The 40th Anniversary Of Their Partnership.*

Jeweler **Harry Winston** gives the $1.5 million, 44.5 carat legendary "cursed" **Hope Diamond**, with its long history of owner disasters, to the Smithsonian sending it via registered mail for a cost of $145.29 for postage and insurance.

A TWO TIMER

Former President Herbert Hoover becomes the only two-time winner of the National Institute of Social Sciences' gold medal for distinguished service to humanity.

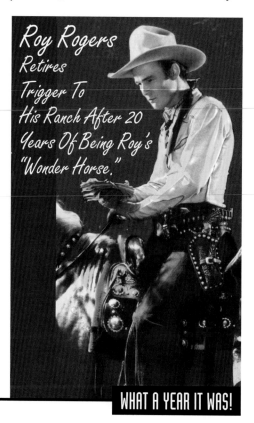

Roy Rogers Retires Trigger To His Ranch After 20 Years Of Being Roy's "Wonder Horse."

William Randolph Hearst's San Simeon Castle Opens As A Museum.

WHAT A YEAR IT WAS!

TIME

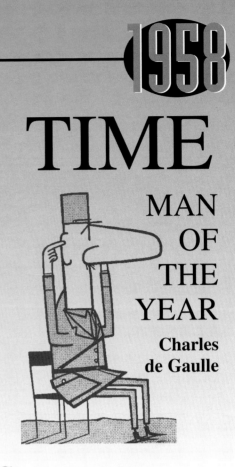

MAN OF THE YEAR

Charles de Gaulle

Marilyn Monroe, Married To Playwright Arthur Miller, Is Recovering After Her Second Miscarriage In Sixteen Months.

Somerset Maugham Celebrates His 84th Birthday On The French Riviera Declaring He Hasn't Had A Story Idea In Years.

YOU THINK YOU OWN THIS BENCH, BUDDY?

Bernard M. Baruch, 88-year old advisor to seven presidents, is honored with a bronze plaque for his favorite bench on Fifth Avenue outside Central Park.
The inscription:
"Elder statesman's bench—reserved for Bernard M. Baruch."

President Eisenhower Celebrates His 68th Birthday With Family And Friends Gathering At Camp David.

Charles de Gaulle Honors **Winston Churchill** In Paris By Bestowing Him With The Cross Of Lorraine.

83-Year Old **Winston Churchill** Goes Out For The First Time Since Being Stricken With Pneumonia And Dines At A Popular Cote d'Azur Restaurant.

NEW WORDS &

ACTION PAINTING
A form of abstract painting in the U.S.

HOT DOG
A race driver.

HULA or HOOLA HOOP
A tubular plastic or metal hoop which is kept rotating around the body by circular movements.

ALASKAPHOBIA
A Texan's fear of something bigger than Texas.

AYM
Angry Young Men- A group of British writers.

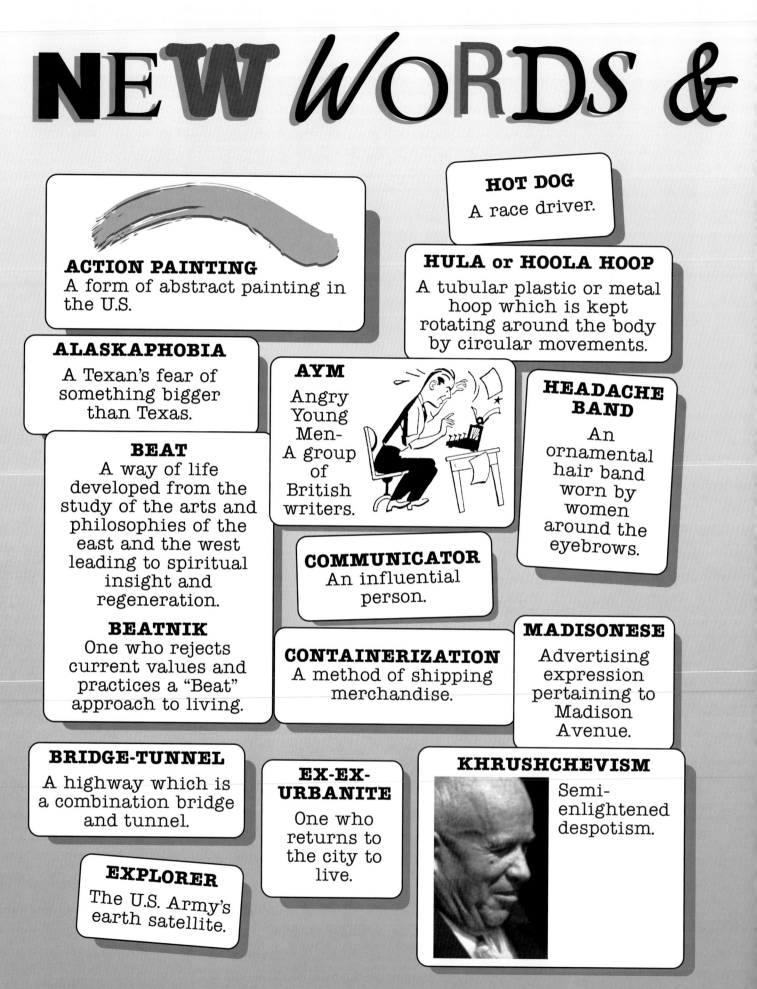

HEADACHE BAND
An ornamental hair band worn by women around the eyebrows.

BEAT
A way of life developed from the study of the arts and philosophies of the east and the west leading to spiritual insight and regeneration.

COMMUNICATOR
An influential person.

BEATNIK
One who rejects current values and practices a "Beat" approach to living.

CONTAINERIZATION
A method of shipping merchandise.

MADISONESE
Advertising expression pertaining to Madison Avenue.

BRIDGE-TUNNEL
A highway which is a combination bridge and tunnel.

EX-EX-URBANITE
One who returns to the city to live.

KHRUSHCHEVISM
Semi-enlightened despotism.

EXPLORER
The U.S. Army's earth satellite.

EXPRESSIONS

MOON DUST
Meteoric particles on the surface of the moon.

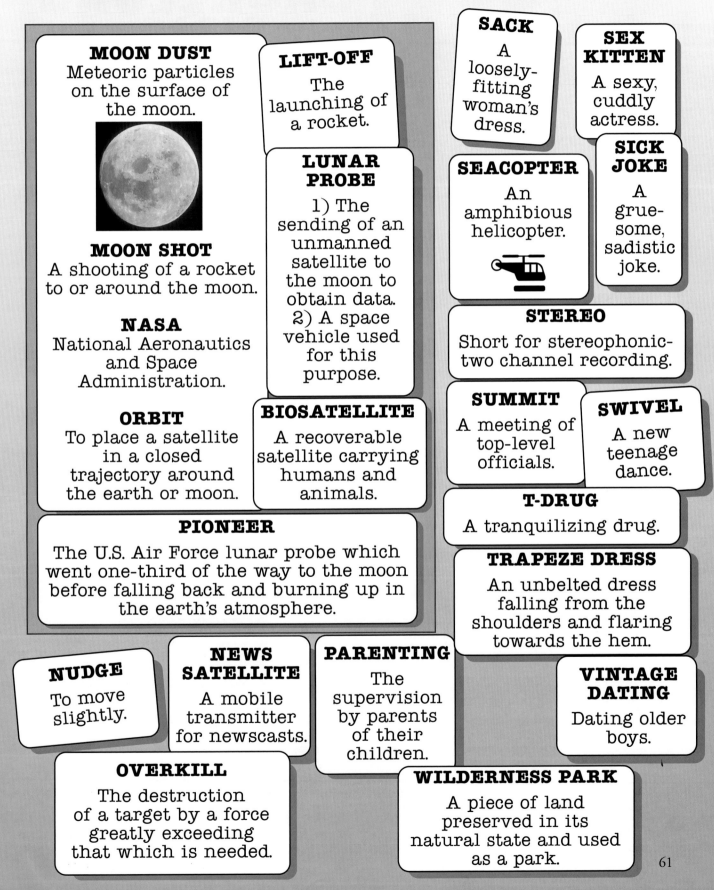

MOON SHOT
A shooting of a rocket to or around the moon.

NASA
National Aeronautics and Space Administration.

ORBIT
To place a satellite in a closed trajectory around the earth or moon.

LIFT-OFF
The launching of a rocket.

LUNAR PROBE
1) The sending of an unmanned satellite to the moon to obtain data.
2) A space vehicle used for this purpose.

BIOSATELLITE
A recoverable satellite carrying humans and animals.

PIONEER
The U.S. Air Force lunar probe which went one-third of the way to the moon before falling back and burning up in the earth's atmosphere.

SACK
A loosely-fitting woman's dress.

SEX KITTEN
A sexy, cuddly actress.

SEACOPTER
An amphibious helicopter.

SICK JOKE
A gruesome, sadistic joke.

STEREO
Short for stereophonic-two channel recording.

SUMMIT
A meeting of top-level officials.

SWIVEL
A new teenage dance.

T-DRUG
A tranquilizing drug.

TRAPEZE DRESS
An unbelted dress falling from the shoulders and flaring towards the hem.

NUDGE
To move slightly.

NEWS SATELLITE
A mobile transmitter for newscasts.

PARENTING
The supervision by parents of their children.

VINTAGE DATING
Dating older boys.

OVERKILL
The destruction of a target by a force greatly exceeding that which is needed.

WILDERNESS PARK
A piece of land preserved in its natural state and used as a park.

1958

BACHELORS
AND THE GIRLS THEY DATE (AND EVENTUALLY MARRY...MAYBE)

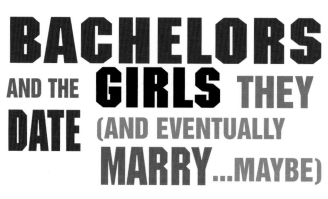

LIKES

- **Long hair**
- **Gentle speech & behavior**
- **Warmth**
- **Teenagers** *(they don't push for the wedding ring)*
- **A potential good mother of their children**
- **Good grooming over beauty** *(beautiful girls tend to be spoiled)*
- **A girl who will occasionally reciprocate a dinner.**
- **Generally likes American women because they are tops in every way, shape and form and are generally the most charming and intelligent women in the world.**

DISLIKES

- **Shorts** *(unless you have great legs)*
- **A girl who tries to be one of the boys.**
- **Aggressiveness**
- **Girls in their twenties who panic about getting married.**
- **A girl using a compact at the table**
- **Girls who plan too far ahead**
- **Girls who brag about expensive dates.**

THE NEUROTIC or LOVE ME, LOVE MY NEUROSIS

1. Neurotic people tend to dissipate energy in unproductive emotional conflicts.

2. Neurotic people succeed despite tendencies not because of them— especially creative artists.

3. Unmarried people tend to be more neurotic than married people.

4. Women tend to be more neurotic than men.

5. Smarter people tend to be less neurotic than their dumber counterparts.

WHAT A YEAR IT WAS!

HUSBAND HUNTING?

A Technique Called **"Brainstorming"** Is Used To Come Up With Ways For Today's **16,000,000 Single Women** To Find A **Husband**

1. Get a dog and walk it.
2. Attend night school—take classes men like.
3. Move to a state with the most men.
4. Read the obituaries to find eligible widowers.
5. Sit on a park bench and feed the pigeons.
6. Get a job in a medical, dental or law office.
7. Become a nurse or airline stewardess.
8. Ask your friends' husbands to introduce you to their bachelor friends.
9. Be friendly to ugly men—a prince could be lurking.
10. Don't be afraid to associate with attractive girls—they may have some leftovers.
11. Tell your friends you want to get married.
12. When travelling stay in small hotels where people may be friendlier.
13. Learn to paint and set up your easel outside an engineering school.

GETTING HIS ATTENTION:

14. Stumble when you walk into a room.
15. Call him once in a while.
16. Wear a band-aid. People always ask what happened.
17. Ask him for some advice.
18. Drop your handkerchief.
19. Stand in a corner and cry softly.
20. If you're at a resort have the bellboy page you.
21. Buy a convertible.
22. Bake a tasty apple pie for the office bachelors.
23. Ask him what kind of perfume you should wear.
24. Wear high heels most of the time—they're sexier.
25. Tell him he's handsome.
26. If you look good in sweaters, wear one every third date.
27. Go on a diet if you need to.
28. Change the shade of your stockings and be sure to keep the seams straight.
29. If he buys you a trinket or accessory, wear it.
30. Use the ashtray; don't crush out cigarettes in coffee cups.
31. Don't be too fussy.
32. Stick to your moral standards.
33. Don't whine—girls who whine stay on the vine.
34. Send his mother a birthday card.
35. On the first date tell him you aren't thinking of marrying.
36. Stand on a busy street corner with a lasso.
37. If he's a fisherman, learn to scale and clean fish.
38. Don't gossip about him.
39. Learn to sew and wear something you have made yourself.
40. Never let him know he's the only one even if you have to stay home.
41. Don't discuss your former boyfriends.
42. Hide your Phi Beta Kappa key—later junior can play with it.
43. Resist the urge to make him over.
44. Remain innocent but not ignorant.
45. Learn to play poker.
46. If he's rich, tell him you like his money—the honesty will intrigue him.
47. Never let him believe your career is more important than marriage.
48. Don't tell dirty jokes.
49. Carry a camera and ask a stranger to take your picture.
50. POINT OUT TO HIM THAT THE DEATH RATE OF SINGLE MEN IS TWICE THAT OF MARRIED MEN!!!

The Flowers That Bloom In The Spring, Tra La

Don Juan — Deep red large double blossoms

Starfire — Medium red large double blossoms

Red Glory — Cherry red semidouble rose

Ivory Fashion — White large semidouble blossoms

Christian Dior — Crimson with scarlet shading

The American Association Of Retired Persons (AARP) Is Established.

MISS AMERICA— *Marilyn Van Derbur,* Denver, Colorado

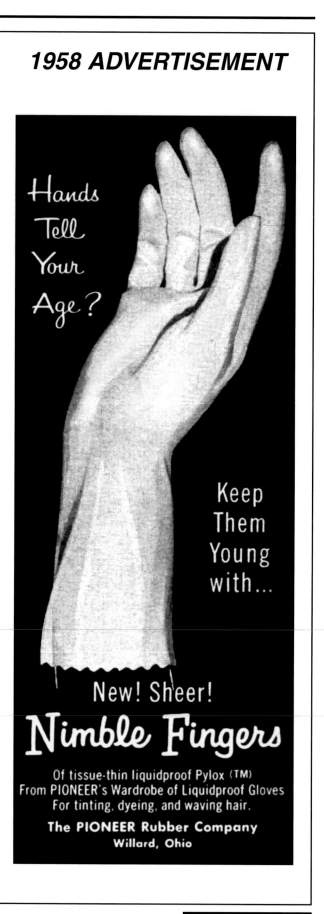

BUT DARLING, I DON'T HAVE A THING TO WEAR
A Peek Inside The Closet Of One Of America's Best Dressed Women

5	Fur Coats	42	Blouses
28	Long Evening & Ball Gowns	3	Umbrellas
14	Cocktail Dresses	1	Pair Of Plastic Rain Boots
19	Suits	29	Sweaters
10	Light Wool Afternoon Dresses	225	Pairs Of Gloves
8	Cotton Or Linen Day Dresses	93	Scarves
		23	Full Slips
6	Cloth Coats	8	Half Slips
1	Fur-Lined Coat	16	Panties
4	Jackets	18	Brassieres
89	Pairs Of Shoes	17	Girdles
8	Short Printed Silk And Chiffon Dresses For Afternoon Wear	5	Dozen Pairs Of Stockings
		28	Handbags
		117	Handkerchiefs
35	Housecoats And Negligees	45	Pairs Of Earrings
37	Nightgowns	38	Necklaces
8	Bed Jackets	28	Clips & Pins
		16	Bracelets

And The Shop 'Till You Drop Awards Go To:

Mrs. Henry Ford II

Mrs. Winston Guest

Mrs. William Randolph Hearst, Jr.

Mrs. William Paley

The Countess Mona von Bismarck

The Duchess of Windsor

THE BURGLAR ALARM
CELEBRATES ITS 100TH BIRTHDAY OF THE FIRST INSTALLATION OF A SYSTEM IN A PRIVATE HOME.

$163,000 IN JEWELS ARE STOLEN FROM THE WINDOW CASES OF NEW YORK'S FAMOUS TIFFANY'S.

WHAT THE WELL DRESSED BALD MAN WILL WEAR

MAKE~UP MOGUL MAX FACTOR OFFERS A $150 IVY LEAGUE HAIRPIECE FOR THAT MADISON AVENUE LOOK.

BETTER EATING THROUGH CHEMISTRY
New York's fancy Waldorf-Astoria Hotel plays host to 200 farm animals including cows, pigs, turkeys, sheep and hens all of whom are guests of the Chas. Pfizer Pharmaceutical Company, which is there to sell farmers, veterinarians and scientists on the advantages of adding chemicals to the diets of food-producing animals.

GOOD TO THE LAST CUP
The famous Vienna Coffee House is soon to be a thing of the past as Pastry Shops (Cafe-Konditorei) begin to replace these traditional meeting places.

HEY HONEY, WHERE'S MY BEER... THE GAME IS STARTIN'
According to the Dean of the University of Chicago's Library School, the English read three times as many books as Americans.

WHAT A YEAR IT WAS!

30 SECONDS FROM CAMERA TO PROJECTOR

FABULOUS ALL-ELECTRIC 8mm MOVIE CAMERA AND PROJECTOR IN ONE

WITTNAUER'S NEW INVENTION— A HIGH-PRECISION PROFESSIONAL-TYPE UNIT THAT CAN SAVE YOU OVER $100

TAKES MOVIES and SHOWS THEM, TOO!

WITTNAUER CINE-TWIN

Here is the amazing new Wittnauer Cine-Twin that you have heard about. This fabulous professional-type all-electric movie camera and projector combination can save you over $100 as compared with separate units of equal quality. ℂ Take the Cine-Twin camera. It's battery driven; no springs to wind—you can take a full reel without stopping, even get into the action yourself. A few of the other exclusive features: a true turret; an oversized optical zoomfinder; a lifetime reserve power indicator which constantly monitors the camera's electronic circuit.

You experience the thrill of taking fascinating professional-quality home movies—steady, flickerless, brilliant in color, correct in speed. A graphic color-coded exposure system guarantees perfect shots. ℂ In 30 seconds your Wittnauer Cine-Twin converts from camera to compact, high-precision projector—ready to regale you with perfectly beautiful, brilliantly colored, life-like home movies. ℂ But, truly, words cannot describe this amazing all-electric movie camera-projector combination. We urge you to see the Wittnauer Cine-Twin for yourself. The price

complete, ready to take and show movies, with f/2.5 standard taking lens and f/1.6 projection lens—$169.50. Telephoto and wide-angle accessory lenses are available at nominal extra cost.

Wittnauer Cameras

BUSINESS

AFL-CIO

Orders An End To All Its Affiliates Dealings With The Teamsters Union.

Dave Beck,

President of the Teamsters, is sentenced to fifteen years on embezzlement charges in a Seattle court room.

First Strike Of International Ladies Garment Workers Union Since 1933 Ends With 3-Year Contract.

WOMEN IN HIGH PLACES

ELLEN-ANN DUNHAM
Vice President, General Electric
"...There will be more women executives in the future...but women's first duty is to the home."

GRACE HILL
President, I. Miller Salons, Inc.
"...More and more key jobs are open to women in the fields of leather, shoe manufacturing and retail stores."

GERALDINE ZORBAUGH
Vice President and General Attorney, CBS
"...If men resent taking orders from me, they don't show it."

MARGARET F. CARLSEN
President, New York Chapter of Chartered Life Underwriters *(First woman to be so elected)*
"...I can get away with more than most men. The men can't say no to me..."

IRS INTRODUCES THE SHORT FORM FEDERAL TAX RETURN FOR PEOPLE WITH ANNUAL INCOMES OF UP TO $10,000.

THE DAYS OF FREE YACHTS AND EUROPEAN TRIPS COME TO AN END

The IRS eases its ruling on expense accounts making a distinction between expense accounts disguised as a "Tax-Free Bonus" vs. legitimate business expenses which are accountable to the employer.

WHAT A YEAR IT WAS!

1958

29 U.S. Oil Companies Indicted for price fixing of crude oil and gasoline prices following the Suez Canal crisis.

Recession-Effected Car Dealers In Flint Michigan Sell 277 Out Of 478 Cars In A One-Day Sale.

Buick – Limited

Cadillac – Eldorado Biarritz

Chevrolet – Impala

Chrysler's 300D

TOYOTA Builds Jeep Factory In Sao Paulo, Brazil.

1958 ADVERTISEMENT

You "feel" the thrill of NEW CAR PERFORMANCE with dependable Low Priced

MUSTANG Replacement ENGINE

Available for most popular makes of cars and trucks. Exchange prices begin at $179.00

Remarkable MUSTANG is precision built, factory-tested to modernize worn out cars and trucks. For amazing new car "get up and go" . . . for double existing mileage. Over a quarter million MUSTANG owners are happy with 10% more power . . . unbelievable savings on gas, oil and repair bills because of advanced engineering geared to this age of space rockets.

Sold on easy payment plan by leading repair shops and car dealers with speedy installation and written, nation-wide guarantee.

MUSTANG ENGINES GARLAND TEXAS

WHAT A YEAR IT WAS!

MANHATTAN

New York's Fifth Avenue Is The Site Of The First Takashimaya Department Store – Japan's Biggest Department Store Chain.

A massive redevelopment of Manhattan's deteriorating West Side around Lincoln Center is launched to include $75 million in concert halls and theatres, a $9 million Fordham University Campus and $65 million in new apartments. The project is expected to take five years and will eventually be the new home for the Metropolitan Opera and Juilliard School of Music.

N·Y

1958 ADVERTISEMENT

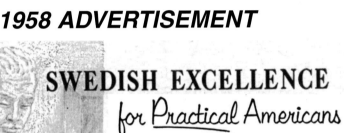

SWEDISH EXCELLENCE
for Practical Americans

VOLVO, the five passenger family sports car, combines the brilliance of Swedish engineering with unbelievable economy and unexcelled performance. Acclaimed by auto experts from coast to coast, VOLVO is truly an automotive investment that pays dividends from the very first drive.

VOLVO, priced with the lowest, is available for immediate delivery. Driving is believing.

Yes, one drive and you'll buy the VOLVO.

A Product of Superb Swedish Engineering

VOLVO

Parts and Service Available Everywhere

QUALITY SETS

VOLVO APART

VOLVO DISTRIBUTING, INC., 15143 W. 8 Mile Rd., Detroit 35, Michigan
SWEDISH MOTOR IMPORT, INC., 1901 Milam St., Houston 2, Texas
AUTO IMPORTS, INC., 13157 Ventura Blvd., Sherman Oaks, California

THE HIGH COST OF SHOPPING

In an effort to boost slumping sales, downtown merchants begin offering parking validations to cover shoppers' parking fees which can be as high as $1.00 for the first hour in New York.

CLEAN:

Who in the World Built this

Big and wonderful and beautiful things have happened to Pontiac—America's Number One Road Car! And they start with an engineering advance no other car has.

Engineering's hottest team has now changed the very foundation of automotive design to bring you *Wide-Track Wheels* and a ride that never before existed! This is the spark that ignited a chain reaction of new ideas. You'll discover fresh new lines . . . vista-lounge interiors with full 360-degree visibility . . . seats *wider than a sofa* . . . True-Contour Air-Cooled

Brakes for smooth, easy, unvarying stops. And the industry's most advanced V-8 reaches new peaks of perfection in Pontiac's spectacular new Tempest 420 V-8—with sound and vibration reduced almost beyond belief.

For *extra* gas mileage there's a new companion engine, optional at no extra cost, that gives you full V-8 power and pep plus the mileage of smaller cars with so-called "economy engines"—*and it uses regular gas!*

If all that sounds like more than enough for one car—that's the *new* Pontiac! Come in to see this new wide-track Pontiac. Bring all the doubts you can muster—you won't leave with a single one!

70

You get the solid quality of Body by Fisher.

Beauty?
PONTIAC!
America's Number ① Road Car

3 Totally New Series • Catalina • Star Chief • Bonneville

EXCLUSIVELY YOURS—*WIDE-TRACK* WHEELS

Wheels moved out a full 5 inches for the widest, steadiest stance in America—better cooling for engine and brakes—lower center of gravity for better grip on the road, safer cornering, smoother ride. *You get the most beautiful roadability in the whole wide world!*

PONTIAC MOTOR DIVISION · GENERAL MOTORS CORPORATION

For the House

Amplifier, 2-speaker hi-fi	$49.95
Chair, folding	$7.95-$9.95
China Cabinet	$149.50
Flashlight	$5.85-$7.50
Frying Pan, automatic	$21.95
Heater, space	$34.95
Hedge Trimmer	$49.50

For the House

Lawnmower	$139.95
Paint Sprayer, electric	$12.95
Power Drill	$29.95
Septic Tank Cleaner	$2.75
Sewing Machine	$89.50
Sprinkler, automatic	$9.95
Tables: Night	$39.50
Dining	$75.50
TV/Hi-Fi System	from $149.90
Vacuum Cleaner	$49.50

Bathroom Essentials

Aftershave Lotion, Old Spice	$1.00
Antacid, Tums	$0.10
Chest Rub	$1.00
Dental Cream	$0.98
Dental Cushions	$0.60
Lip Balm	$0.35
Shaver, electric: Men's	$24.95
Women's	$14.95
Toothbrush	$0.69
Toothpaste	$0.79

RING A DING DING

Phone Rates:

United States to Europe
$12.00 for 3 minutes

Boston to New York
$1.05 (person-to-person)

Cleveland to San Francisco
$2.35 (station-to-station)

WHAT A YEAR IT WAS!

Assorted Necessities

Airfare, New York-Paris,
round trip $489.60
Album, Benny Goodman,
"Swing Into Spring" $1.29
Camera, 3-way flash $7.50
Car, Fiat 600 . . . . $1,330.00
Car Washing Detergent $0.75
Cigars, Dutch Masters . . . . 2/$0.25
Dictionary, Webster's $5.00
Dog Vitamins $0.79
Dunkin' Donuts Franchise,
min. investment $30,000.00

Clothes

Boots, Rain $2.00
Bra $3.95-6.50
Coat, Men's
Trench $20.95
Sportscoat . . . . from $39.95
Cufflinks &
Tie Clip Set $6.00

Assorted Necessities

Eyeglass Hearing Aid $145.00
Lighter with windguard $3.95
Magazines:
"Sports Illustrated" . . . . $0.25 per iss.
"Newsweek" . . . . $6.00 per yr.
"Saturday Evening Post" . . . . $0.15 per iss.
"Life" . . . . $7.75 per yr.
Magic Marker $0.77
Movie Camera/Projector $169.50
Pen Set, 14k gold $25.00
Slide Projector $84.50
Slide Viewer $7.95
Spot Remover $0.29
Towel, Bath $1.59
Tuition, Harvard $1,250.00
Watch, Men's . . . . from $59.50

Clothes

Dress . . . . from $7.98
Sandals, Dr. Scholls:
Children's $6.95
Adult's $9.95
Shirt, sports
Boy's $2.98
Men's $3.98
Shoes,
Men's $12.95-21.95
Slacks,
Men's . . . . from $14.95
Socks $1.00

AVERAGE YEARLY WAGES

President of the United States
$100,000

Vice President of the United States
$35,000

"These *National* registers help us serve you better by figuring your change!"

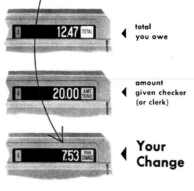

◄ total you owe

◄ amount given checker (or clerk)

◄ **Your Change**

Store owners must see this new register to appreciate its advantages. Call your nearest National office for a demonstration today!

"*National* Change Computing Cash Registers return over 100% a year on our investment."

—HILL GROCERY CO., *Birmingham, Ala.*

"During the past 47 years we have built our chain of stores by constantly seeking ways to serve our customers better, and to reduce our costs of operation. We started to install National Change Computing Registers soon after they were placed on the market.

"The Nationals show — at the top of the register and on the receipt — *every* step in the transaction . . . and they enforce accuracy in every step. They stop mistakes in figuring change. Cash shortages are practically eliminated. Time is saved so customers are served

faster and better, which builds confidence and good will.

"These savings and benefits combined return us more than 100% annually on our investment in Nationals."

Sophie President
Hill Grocery Company

THE NATIONAL CASH REGISTER COMPANY, DAYTON 9, OHIO
989 OFFICES IN 94 COUNTRIES

AVERAGE MONTHLY EXPENSES

	$8,000 YEARLY SALARY	$25,000 YEARLY SALARY
Mortgage	$102.86	$333.57
Food	$94.15	$173.33
Baby-sitter	$10.00	$43.33
Taxes	$98.00	$415.48
Electricity	$8.00	$46.83
Newspapers & Magazines	$4.10	$6.66
Telephone	$10.00	$11.97

Ever wonder how many hours you have to work to buy your favorite items? It actually takes fewer work hours today to buy goods than it did 10 years ago.

	1948 No. of Hours	1958 No. of Hours
Quart of Milk	10	7
Pound of Coffee	23	22
Refrigerator	176	108
Radio	17	10
Automobile	1100	1090

AMERICAN EXPRESS

Issues Its First Credit Card For Charging Travel And Hotel Expenses.

INSTANT FLIGHT INFORMATION now available to passengers in four languages at Brussels' National Airport on closed-circuit television sets positioned throughout the new air terminal.

Agreement Signed In Moscow Between European Airways and Soviet Aeroflot For Direct London-Moscow Air Service.

First Transatlantic Jet Airliner Crossing Made By British Overseas Airways From New York to London In Record 6 Hours 12 Minutes.

AVERAGE WEEKLY WAGES

Bank Employee	$65.88
Hotel Employee	$45.60
Jewelry Manufacturing Employee	$75.70
Motion Picture Distribution Employee	$98.65
Publishing Employee	$97.38
Telephone Employee	$79.31

AVERAGE WEEKLY EARNINGS PER AREA

New York	$83.02
Ohio	$93.27
California	$96.90
Kentucky	$79.40
Colorado	$90.90

AVERAGE HOURLY WAGES

Construction	$2.99
Automobiles	$2.48
Mining	$2.22

Drop Up To 40% On General Electric Appliances In Price Wars Around The Country Following Its Announcement Of The End Of Fair Trade Pricing.

Toy maker A.C. Gilbert Co. reports that for the first time sales of scientific toys are higher than sales of its american flyer trains.

THE END OF THE LINE

Despite its efforts to lure passengers by offering deluxe service, gourmet food and club cars, Baltimore & Ohio Railroad is forced to shut down its New York/Baltimore run due to grave financial losses of up to $5 million yearly.

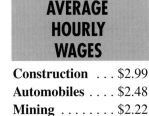

1958

UP IN SMOKE

Pepsi-Cola Bottling Co. of Los Angeles launches a sky-writing bingo game with prizes of up to $25,000 weekly.

☼ SUN & FUN

Columbia Broadcasting System and the Los Angeles Turf Club joint venture on the development of a 28-acre amusement park in Santa Monica, California to be called Pacific Ocean Park.

Trader Joe's Begins Operations In Los Angeles Under The Name Pronto Convenience Stores.

PASS THE POI

The Eighth Trader Vic's Restaurant Opens In New York.

Developer James Rouse Builds One Of The First Enclosed Shopping Malls In Glen Burnie, Maryland.

W.L. Gore & Associates Begins Operations And Introduces "Miracle Fabric" Gore-Tex, A Waterproof Lightweight Fabric.

OH SAY CAN YOU SEE

Dixie Flag Manufacturing Company Begins Manufacturing American Flags And Banners.

Dan and Frank Carney open Pizza Hut in Wichita, Kansas.

Amidst Threats Of War By Rebel Leader Fidel Castro, Under Tight Security A Gala Party Celebrates Opening Of New Luxury Hotel The Havana Hilton.

PASSINGS

Banker Arthur B. Eisenhower, older brother of the President, expert in grain finance, dies at age 71.

John Randolph Hearst, newspaper executive, dies in the Virgin Islands at age 67.

Pabst beer giant Fred Pabst, creator of the Holstein-Friesian cattle breed, dies at age 88.

One-time head of musical giant EMI, Sir Louis Sterling, generous philanthropist who gave away nearly $3 million during his lifetime, dies in London at the age of 79.

Financier and former director of U.S. Steel and W.R. Grace companies, John Shafer Phipps dies at the age of 84.

U.S. industrialist, engineer and inventor Charles Franklin Kettering, whose many inventions include the electric cash register and high-compression engine, holder of approximately 140 patents with an estimated personal worth of $150,000,000 dies at age 82.

James Dole, whose surname is synonymous with Hawaiian pineapple and the renowned company he began in 1901, dies in Honolulu at age 80.

Founder of the mammoth Zenith Radio corporation, Commander Eugene F. McDonald, Jr., who created his company with two ham radios, dies at age 68.

Heavyweight champ turned businessman Harry Wills dies at age 68.

KENTILE VINYL
ON TODAY'S SMARTEST FLOORS

Friendly atmosphere of this charming Early American décor was inspired by the rich, nutty tones of the floor. Kentile Corktone® Vinyl Asbestos Tile is available in light, medium, and dark shades.

So wonderfully warm looking! So delightfully informal! KENTILE®Corktone Vinyl Asbestos Tile with the rich, nutty tones customers love. And how you'll love its economy. You see, its easier care and longer wear make it pay for itself in lower maintenance costs. It's greaseproof . . . stain resistant . . . won't pit either.

Interested? Your Kentile Floor Contractor is listed under FLOORS in your classified phone book. Kentile Floors are available in Vinyl Asbestos (Kenflex®), Solid Vinyl, Cushion-back Vinyl, Cork, Rubber and Asphalt Tile . . . over 175 decorator colors! © 1958, Kentile, Inc., Brooklyn 15, New York.

SCIENCE & MEDICINE

AMERICA LAUNCHES ITS FIRST EARTH SATELLITE – THE EXPLORER.

The Atlas Ballistic Missile guides itself into orbit to become by far the biggest artificial moon. It carries a tape recording broadcasting to the world President Eisenhower's message of peace.

Darwin's "The Origin Of The Species" Celebrates Its 100th Year Of Publication.

Scientists in London discover a 3-1/2 year old chimp whose art work resembles that of its human counterpart.

Nobel Prizes

PHYSICS

PAVEL A. CHERENKOV, *USSR*

ILYA M. FRANK, *USSR*

IGOR Y. TAMM, *USSR*

CHEMISTRY

FREDERICK SANGER, *Great Britain*

MEDICINE

GEORGE W. BEADLE, *USA*

EDWARD L. TATUM, *USA*

JOSHUA LEDERBERG, *USA*

LINUS PAULING Awarded Full Membership In The Soviet Academy Of Sciences.

Sweden's George C. de Hevesy is winner of the 1958 Atoms For Peace Award.

According to a paper presented at an International Congress of Radiation Research by a scientist from Brookhaven National Laboratory at Upton, Long Island, New York, there is no conclusive evidence that prolonged stress shortens one's life span.

KEEP YOUR SUNNY SIDE UP

A solar energy system that uses the sun's rays to cool as well as to provide heat is installed in a house under construction in Phoenix. It also provides a year-round supply of hot water and heats the swimming pool.

Peaceful Pears

The United States Rubber Company introduces a chemical "tranquilizer" to keep the plants "relaxed" during stressful conditions such as heat spells, sudden cold snaps, excessive rain or drought.

SOME LIKE IT SWEET

According to research conducted at Rutgers University into the eating habits of mosquitoes, the little creatures have a built-in detection system which leads them to thin, warm, sweet tasting people for their midnight munchies.

SOME LIKE IT DEEP

Chief of Naval Research, Rear Admiral Rawson Bennett, reveals plans for the development of a bathyscaphe capable of carrying scientists and laboratory equipment six miles down to the deepest trench in the ocean floor.

HEY, I'VE GOT THIS GREAT BRIDGE FOR SALE

In a trial held in Federal Court in Brooklyn where plaintiffs claim that the 3,000,000 pounds of DDT sprayed over their property in Nassau and Suffolk counties resulted in contamination of their soil and their milk herds and had endangered their health, a government scientist testifies that examinations of employees working in DDT manufacturing plants showed no ill effects after having absorbed large amounts of the chemical.

WHAT A YEAR IT WAS!

1958

According To Werner von Braun, U.S. Space Research Is At Least Two Years Behind The Soviets.

John Foster Dulles tells the Foreign Affairs Committee that the Soviets will probably be the first to land on the moon.

Soviet News Agency Tass Confirms That Sputnik I Disintegrated Early In The Year.

U.S. Navy Successfully Launches Vanguard I Out Of Cape Canaveral Making It The Second U.S. Satellite.

Soviets Successfully Launch Sputnik III.

● ●

The Navy Tries And Fails Six Times To Orbit Vanguard II.

Soviet Union Reports Successfully Sending Two Dogs 281 Miles In Space With A Safe Return.

● ●

Third Successful Satellite, Explorer III, Is Fired Into Orbit From Cape Canaveral.

The first human voice heard from space is President Eisenhower's recorded Christmas message which is beamed from Project Score, America's first communications satellite.

● ●

U.S. Launches Its Fourth Satellite, Explorer IV, To Explore Cosmic Ray Data.

● ●

America's First Moon Shot Ends In Failure When Rocket Explodes At 50,000 Feet.

Advanced Research Projects Agency is established in Washington, becoming first U.S. space body.

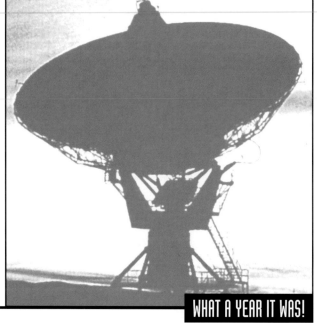

WHAT A YEAR IT WAS!

British and American scientists produce fusion by warming atoms to 100 million degrees.

THE U.S. ATOMIC ENERGY COMMISSION LAUNCHES NEW SERIES OF NUCLEAR TESTS IN NEVADA.

The "Sea Wolf," a U.S. atomic powered submarine, cruises 60 days underwater setting a new record.

THE PENTAGON
INTRODUCES THE
NIKE-HERCULES,
THE FIRST SURFACE TO AIR NUCLEAR MISSILE TO BE INCORPORATED INTO THE U.S. CONTINENTAL DEFENSE SYSTEM.

EIGHT NIKE MISSILES EXPLODE AT A NEW JERSEY BASE KILLING TEN PEOPLE.

The "TRITON," World's Largest Sub, Is Launched In Groton, Connecticut.

U.S. ATOMIC SUBMARINE
NAUTILUS
COMPLETES FIRST KNOWN VOYAGE UNDER NORTH POLAR ICE CAP.

The U.S. Air Force chooses the Thor Missile over Jupiter for mass production as ICBM.

The United States Unveils Its X-15 Rocket Plane.

U.S. Fires ICBM 6,000 Miles In Record Test.

84

Believe It or Not!

"MOWING" THE MOISTURE OFF GOLF GREENS!

NOW GOLFERS NEEDN'T PUTT ON SLOW, SOGGY GREENS. THIS MACHINE, OPERATED LIKE A POWER MOWER, QUICKLY DRIES THE GRASS. REVOLVING SPONGES SOAK UP MOISTURE,"WRING IT OUT"INTO A TANK. FOR MAXIMUM EFFECTIVENESS, THE SPONGES ARE LINKED TO THE ENGINE BY A PRECISION <u>ROLLER CHAIN</u> DRIVE FROM B-W'S **MORSE CHAIN.** IT GIVES SURE, SLIP-FREE POWER REQUIRED FOR PROPER WATER PICK-UP AND FAST OPERATION.

OVER 200,000 MENTALLY ILL RESTORED TO HEALTH LAST YEAR!

ONCE THOUGHT TO BE HOPELESS, MENTAL ILLNESS IS NOW BEING CONQUERED IN AN EVER LARGER PERCENTAGE OF CASES. AUTHORITIES REPORT 7 OUT OF 10 CASES CAN BE RESTORED TO HAPPY, USEFUL LIVING. NEW DRUGS, THERAPY AND BETTER UNDERSTANDING HAVE MADE THIS POSSIBLE. BUT PREVENTING MENTAL ILLNESS IS BETTER THAN CURES. NEW FREE BOOKLET GIVES HELPFUL INFORMATION. WRITE FOR **"HOW TO DEAL WITH YOUR TENSIONS,"** BOX 2500, NEW YORK 1, N.Y.

For 30 years Borg-Warner has been serving the automotive industry with vital operating parts. These include:

Fuel injection
Automatic and standard transmissions
Overdrive
Clutches
Universal joints
Differentials
Timing chains
Carburetors

Borg-Warner skill and ingenuity also benefit almost every American every day through many other fields, including:

Aviation. Every type of military and commercial aircraft contains essential B-W parts.
Nucleonics. B-W designed parts are at work in almost every U.S. reactor.
Farm. 9 out of 10 modern farms use B-W equipped machines.
Home. Millions of homes use B-W building materials, equipment, appliances.
Oil. Every oil field has B-W equipment.

EXPLOSIVE CAPSULE SHAPES STEEL BETTER THAN 2500-TON PRESS!

CALLED "CONCUSSION FORMING," IT'S A NEW METAL-WORKING TECHNIQUE USED BY **B-W'S INGERSOLL-KALAMAZOO** FOR MISSILE PARTS, AMONG OTHER THINGS. THE CHARGE USED WILL FIT IN YOUR HAND, YET ITS EXPLOSIVE FORCE CAN FORM 1/2" THICK STEEL SHEETS INTO INTRICATE SHAPES. SHOCK WAVES DO THE WORK OF A HUGE PRESS...SQUEEZE THE METAL INTO THE DIE TO PRODUCE SHAPES IMPOSSIBLE WITH OTHER FORMING METHODS. EVEN NEEDED CUT-OUTS AND HOLES CAN BE PUNCHED IN THE SAME OPERATION.

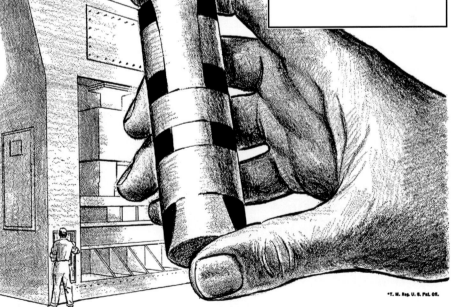

*T. M. Reg. U. S. Pat. Off.

1958

Climbing Expedition Led By Sir Edmund P. Hillary Reaches The South Pole After 1,200 Mile Overland Trip From Scott Station On The Ross Sea Coast.

Bacteria thought to be between 800 to 3,000 years old discovered at the South Pole.

A British Team Lead By Vivian E. Fuchs Completes A 2,100 Trek Across The Antarctic Continent.

The development of an electronic flash attached to a gastroscope makes it possible to photograph the interior of the stomach.

A 100-million-year old fossil skeleton of the largest flesh-eating reptile in the sea has been reconstructed at Harvard's Museum of Comparative Zoology.

A Millipede With 700 Legs Is Discovered In A Panama Valley.

A solar furnace is tested at the California Institute of Technology.

WORLD'S LARGEST ATOMIC POWER STATION OPENS IN SIBERIA.

INTEGRATED CIRCUITRY

Is invented – Jack Kilby describes the "Monolithic Idea," the basis of the microchip.

THE VAN ALLEN BELT

James Van Allen describes two belts of cosmic radiation around the earth.

PASSINGS

Jean Frederick Joliet-Curie, physicist, head of the French Atomic Energy and French Communist organizations, French resistance member during World War II and winner, along with his wife Irene, of 1935's Nobel Prize for chemistry, dies at age 58.

The biggest man in American Medical Association's history, 1,041 pound Robert Earl Hughes dies at age 32.

Psychologist John Watson, founder of the behaviorism method of psychology dies at age 80.

Founder of England's first birth-control clinic and the first woman science lecturer at Manchester University, Dr. Marie C. Stopes dies at age 78.

Wolfgang Pauli, who won a Nobel prize for his Exclusion Principle and worked with the Neutrino, dies in Switzerland at age 58.

WHAT A YEAR IT WAS!

MEDICINE

The American life span has increased 22 years since 1900 with the Netherlands having the longest life expectancy of 72.5 years.

According To Tests Conducted By Boston Biochemists, Vitamin C Is The Key To Speedy Healing Of Wounds.

According To A Public Health Service Survey, Illness Strikes Americans On An Average Of 16 Days A Year.

A study conducted by the National Institute of Health reveals that the death rate among nearly 200,000 U.S. veterans is significantly higher for smokers than non-smokers.

PRESIDENT EISENHOWER'S
PERSONAL PHYSICIAN GIVES HIS PRESCRIPTION FOR A LONG, HAPPY LIFE

(1) Be Happy With Your Work   (2) Eat Healthfully
(3) Take Time Out During The Day To Relax And Rest
(4) Overcome Extremist Tendencies
(5) Get A Good Night's Sleep
(6) Don't Overindulge In Drinking Or Smoking
(7) Exercise In Moderation
(8) Avoid Fats As You Get Older
(9) Avoid Stress And Strain
(10) Be Philosophical About Things That Happen

1958

Medical Students Expect To Earn An Average Of $15,000 Ten Years After Graduation.

PROFILE OF A DOCTOR

Age: 40's
No. Daily Patients: 26
Work Day: 8 hours
    (6 in office, 2 in house calls)
Office Visit: $4.00
House Call: $5.00
Average Income: $20,000 yearly
    (West Coast)

The medical specialty favored by most women physicians is Pediatrics, followed by Psychiatry, Neurology, Obstetrics and Gynecology.

The Average Adult American Is Moderately Obese.

The Dallas County Medical Society kicks off the first health education campaign of its kind called "Dallas Fights Its Waistline" and aims at the estimated 160,000 Dallas citizens who are too big for their britches.

♥ DuMont Television's station WABD telecasts first live heart operation from New York City's Bellevue Medical Center. Patient is a three-year old girl.

♥ Montreal Heart Surgeon, Dr. Arthur Vineberg, Invents A Mechanical Heart Massager.

♥ Cold Drinks Thought To Trigger An Angina Attack.

♥ Experiments done with rabbits given a diet high in cholesterol show a significant drop in hardening of the arteries for those rabbits who regularly exercised on a treadmill.

Average Cost Of A Hospital Stay:
$26.81
per day.

♥ A blood loss monitor is developed by Dr. Harry H. LaVeen, Chief of Surgery at the Veterans Administration Hospital in Brooklyn, New York.

♥ A team of Canadian surgeons develop an artery stapler which tests successfully on pigs.

THE NATIONAL ASSOCIATION OF CHIROPODISTS CHANGES ITS NAME TO THE AMERICAN PODIATRY ASSOCIATION.

WHAT A YEAR IT WAS!

cures & epidemics

Measles Vaccine Developed By John Enders.

300 Detroit children ages 2-1/2 months to 5 years are successfully tested with a four-in-one-vaccine against polio, whooping cough, diphtheria and tetanus.

With 800,000 of its 3 million citizens ignoring Salk vaccine immunization shots, Detroit declares a health emergency as it fights the city's worst polio outbreak since 1955.

THE AMERICAN MEDICAL ASSOCIATION AND U.S. PUBLIC HEALTH SERVICE ANNOUNCE THE AVAILABILITY OF A NEW TUBERCULOSIS VACCINE DEVELOPED BY THE FRENCH.

ORAL POLIO VACCINE SUCCESSFULLY FIELD-TESTED IN AFRICA DURING FOUR EPIDEMIC OUTBREAKS.

In a mosquito-spread epidemic sweeping the Far East, encephalitis, known as "Sleeping Sickness," attacks 7,000, killing more than 1,600 people in South Korea, Japan and Formosa.

Hospitals trying to fight the Staphylococcus Aureus germ, a tough penicillin-resistant strain causing patients to pick up serious secondary diseases during their stay.

Phenylalanine mustard being used successfully in New Orleans in the treatment of "black cancer" or melanoma.

Louisiana's Governor Earl K. Long Signs Legislation Requiring Blood Banks To Label All Plasma By Race.

FOR COLORED ONLY

GARLIC JUICE

shown to stop spread of cancer in mice in laboratory experiments performed in a Cleveland University.

MELATONIN
First Hormone Ever Isolated From The Pineal Gland.

1958

Birth Control Pills For Women Begin Clinical Trials.

A new hormone called Provera has been synthesized by the Upjohn Company that may help prevent miscarriage or premature birth.

According to research done on rats, females who drink alcohol during pregnancy lessen their babies' learning abilities.

According to a Chicago pediatrician, competitive sports for pre-teenagers are dangerous especially tackle football, boxing and wrestling which can result in permanent injuries and could put excessive strain on heart, lungs and kidneys.

7,000 infants born in West Germany and England with severe birth defects linked to Thalidomide, a drug sold in Europe as a sleeping pill and treatment for morning sickness during pregnancy.

*i*n a study conducted at Children's Hospital of Philadelphia in conjunction with Princeton University, religious youngsters are more anxious about death than their non-religious counterparts.

KITTY CORNER

According to orthopedists, there seems to be a relationship between an infant's sleeping position and deformities that occur later with a recommendation that an infant be trained to sleep on its side, alternating after each feeding by propping a small pillow behind the shoulders and hips to prevent rolling onto its back.

More Than 70% Of The Nation's Teenagers Still Suffer From Acne.

Dr. Ian Donald, professor at the University of Glasgow, experiments with the use of ultrasound to diagnose pregnancy stating that further development is needed before the technique will be successful at diagnosing benign or malignant lumps and masses.

Survey Shows Trend Away From Breast Feeding And Toward The Use Of Bottles.

RESEARCHERS DETERMINE THAT A GRAVE EMOTIONAL BLOW CAN LEAD TO PHYSICAL ILLNESS.

A five-year study of 2,000 people reveals that executives have less hypertension and arteriosclerosis than nonexecutive office workers of comparable sex, age and work environment.

HYPNOSIS is used successfully on college students in Tennessee to remove deep-seated blocks in the unconscious resulting in an average 15% higher grades than students who are not hypnotized.

Swiss psychologist Carl Jung writes that postwar sightings of flying saucers and other UFOs were not hallucinations.

A behavioral approach to psychology is developed by Joseph Wolpe in "Psychotherapy By Reciprocal Inhibition."

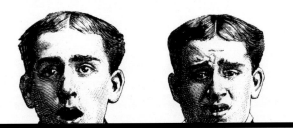

HIGH COST OF BEING A GENIUS

According to a study done by Britain's Dr. V.B. Green-Armytage 9 out of 10 of the world's geniuses suffered from alcoholism, narcotic addiction, tuberculosis or mental instability. In addition most were short, impotent or had little sex drive. There have been few or no women geniuses. Included in the genius group are Lord Nelson, Shakespeare, Voltaire, Chopin, Shelley, Raphael and Einstein.

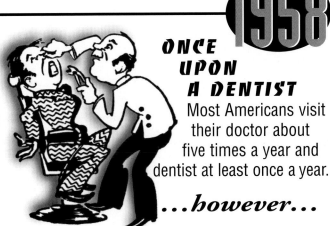

ONCE UPON A DENTIST
Most Americans visit their doctor about five times a year and dentist at least once a year.

...however...

According to a national health survey conducted by the Public Health Service, four out of ten Americans have not been to the dentist for three years or more.

According to a survey by the American Dental Association, although most Americans have a toothbrush, very few actually use it.

The American Dental Association says due to the influence of television, we have become a nation of nibblers thus increasing sugar intake and the resultant increase in tooth decay.

According to Harvard Dental School, excessive gum-chewing damages dental work including jackets, crowns and fillings.

1958 ADVERTISEMENT

More to enjoy

Their new car radio—Motorola Model GV800, 8 transistors. Custom-fits most any 12-volt car. Volumatic®. Golden Voice® speaker sound. 24-karat gold-plated front and pushbuttons. Specifications subject to change without notice.

Car radio that's come a long way. Our Motorola Golden Voice car radio, being enjoyed here, is the first all-transistor set to custom-fit most cars. Thanks to its eight transistors, it takes less power than your dash lights. Needs no warm up, either. Just touch one of the gold-plated pushbuttons, and music comes on instantly. Motorola car radios have come a long way since we made our first one, 30 years ago. They've become one of America's best-known brand names. But we're still pioneering to give you *More to enjoy* on the road!

MOTOROLA

Motorola Radio

new products & inventions

GERMANY

Sends Us A Car Antenna That Automatically Rises When You Turn On The Radio And Retracts When You Turn The Radio Off.

A delayed-action switch that keeps auto headlights on for one minute after turning them off is marketed by Cauhorn Distributing Co. of Detroit.

A British company introduces the "PETA," a radar speed-check device designed to hone in on a specific speeding car.

The Firestone Tire and Rubber Co. develops a spare tire that takes up less than one-third the trunk space used by the current conventional spare tire and fits into a recess in the bottom of the trunk.

Gregory Sales Co. of Cleveland, Ohio offers an automatic car alarm that sounds like a car horn that gets tripped if anyone tampers with the car.

MOTOROLA

previews a portable battery-powered television set at Chicago's Home Furnishings Show expected to be available for distribution in about two years.

Emerson Radio & Phonograph Company markets the world's first battery-powered clock radio.

Two German engineers invent a transistorized portable radio designed to fit inside the user's ear without connecting wires.

Zenith Radio Corp.

designs a hearing mechanism which is embedded in an eye-glass frame where silicon cells convert light energy into an electrical current which activates the device.

The Revere Camera Company of Chicago introduces a new fully automatic still camera that adjusts to different lighting conditions.

1958

A ZIPPERLESS ZIPPER

developed by the American Velcro Corp. of Manchester, New Hampshire is made of two strips of nylon fabric – one strip made of tiny hooks, the other a mass of tiny loops which close when the two strips are pressed together.

PLASTIC

BAGEL SLICING

BECOMES SAFER NOW THAT THE INTERNATIONAL PRODUCTS COMPANY OF MIAMI HAS INTRODUCED A PLASTIC BAGEL HOLDER.

THE WHIRLEY CORP. **PLASTIC** OF ST. LOUIS MARKETS ITS NEW

"WHIRLEY-WHIRLER,"

A SPINNING PLATE OF UNBREAK-ABLE PLASTIC FOR SALE AT $1.49.

Using mylar, a strong plastic film on which raised lines are etched in, l in, a drawing kit for the he blind is developed. d.

United States Rubber Co.

Introduces A 10-Passenger Portable Life Raft Inflatable Within 30 Seconds.

"FRAME-UPS," INVISIBLE CORNER PLASTIC HOLDERS DESIGNED TO GIVE SUPPORT TO PICTURES ON ANY STANDARD SIZE FRAME IS OFFERED FOR THE FIRST TIME.

PLASTIC TEST TUBE RACKS REPLACE WOODEN RACKS.

A PLASTIC LAMINATING KIT TO SEAL DOCUMENTS SUCH AS A DRIVER'S LICENSE IS MADE AVAILABLE BY THE LOUELL PRODUCTS COMPANY OF NEW YORK.

THERMOMETER

AN OUTDOOR TRANSPARENT, PLASTIC THERMOMETER THAT STICKS TO THE OUTSIDE OF THE WINDOW IS NOW AVAILABLE THROUGH SUNSET HOUSE IN LOS ANGELES, CALIFORNIA.

Bauer & Black of Chicago develop a transparent flesh color bandage.

WHAT A YEAR IT WAS!

The Disposable Bic Pen Comes To America Via France.

The Ropex Company develops the "Broad-Scriber," a brush-tip fountain pen combining the flexibility of a brush with the rigidity of a pen for use in fine detail work.

A 4-Color Ball-Point Retractable Pen Is Introduced By Koh-I-Noor.

THROW-AWAY LINES

1. Disposable plastic shower caps developed by the Anderson Company of Oconomowoc, Wisconsin.

2. From the Rochester Razor Corp. of Rochester, New York comes the disposable shaving kit no bigger than a pack of cigarettes.

3. Disposable shoe shine pads for a quick shine made available through Pet Chemicals, Inc. of Miami, Florida.

An electric shoe polisher with a bristle brush that spins is being offered by Dremel Manufacturing Co. of Racine, Wisconsin.

ROUX

introduces color curl in six shades available for $1.50.

The Risdon Manufacturing Co. of Naugatuck, Connecticut develops an aerosol perfume dispenser the size of a lipstick case.

A portable, cordless, rechargeable electric shaver called the
ROYALMATIC DELUXE
is developed in Los Angeles.

The world's first push-button soap which is dispensed from a spray can is developed by Angelique & Co. of Wilton, Connecticut.

Automatic butter patty wrapper developed by Butter-Pak of Denver, Colorado.

A portable, folding bicycle that fits into the trunk of a car is introduced by World Service Enterprises of New York City.

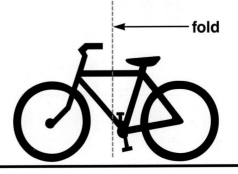
← fold

1958

LEVER BROTHERS INTRODUCES PINK-STRIPED CANDY-CANE TOOTHPASTE FOR KIDS.

SWEET SMELL OF SUCCESS

Sweet 'n' Low

hits the market taking the sugar out of tea and coffee cups all over the country.

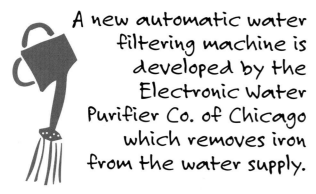

A new automatic water filtering machine is developed by the Electronic Water Purifier Co. of Chicago which removes iron from the water supply.

Method Developed For Freezing And Storing Milk For Up To A Year.

The Pet Milk Co. of St. Louis, Missouri introduces a powdered fat-free milk that dissolves instantly when mixed in water.

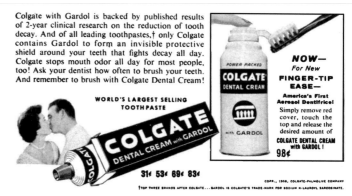

Portable ultra-violet lamps are made available to art galleries and dealers for use in detecting forgeries.

Westinghouse Develops A New Cylindrical Shape Bulb That Diffuses Light.

FOR NIGHT OWLS

A WRISTWATCH THAT LIGHTS UP AT THE PRESS OF A BUTTON IS INTRODUCED BY THE BOREL WATCH CO. OF KANSAS CITY, MISSOURI.

RCA

Develops An Easy To Use Stereophonic-Tape Cartridge.

A fully transistorized miniature tape recorder operating on four batteries is imported from West Germany.

UNITED AIRLINES

at O'Hare Field, Chicago uses the first aero-gangplank designed by Lockheed Air Terminals, Inc. of Burbank, California, a covered, three-section elevated ramp that telescopes out from terminal to the door of the plane in 90 seconds allowing passengers direct entry from the terminal to the plane without going outside.

An automatic currency changer has been developed by the A.B.T. Manufacturing Corp. of Chicago, Illinois which returns change for a dollar bill.

A full newspaper page can now be typed out in 8 minutes due to the development of a new automatic printer.

A One-Piece Loudspeaker Telephone Is Invented In Sweden.

PASSINGS

Malcolm Lockheed, aeronautical engineer and founder with brother Allan of Lockheed Aircraft Co., dies at age 70.

ARCHIT

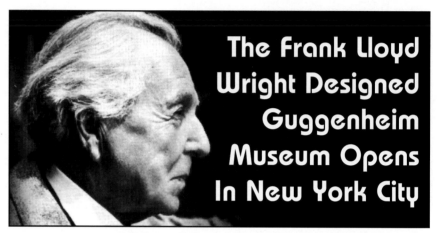

The Frank Lloyd Wright Designed Guggenheim Museum Opens In New York City

The New UNESCO Home In Paris Is A Collaborative Effort Of International Architects And Artists.

At The Brussels World's Fair Innovative Architectural Designs Can Be Viewed From Around The World. Winners According To International Architects Are:

1st Place	Czechoslovakia
2nd Place	Belgium
3rd Place	Great Britain
4th Place	U.S. & West Germany

PASSING

Quonset hut designer Frederick Wierk, whose creation has been home to millions of GI's, dies at age 57.

ECTURE

Hundreds Of American Architects Choose Their Favorite Buildings:

BUILDING	ARCHITECT
General Motors Technical Center, Detroit	Eero Saarinen
Rockefeller Center, Manhattan	Reinhard & Hofmeister Corbett, Harrison & MacMurray Hood & Fouilhoux Harrison & Abramovitz
Lever House, Manhattan	Skidmore, Owings & Merrill
Robie House, Chicago	Frank Lloyd Wright
S.C. Johnson & Son, Inc., headquarters – Racine, WI	Frank Lloyd Wright
"Falling Water," summer house – Bear Run, PA	Frank Lloyd Wright
Solomon R. Guggenheim Museum, Manhattan	Frank Lloyd Wright
Carson Pirie Scott, department store – Chicago	Adler & Sullivan
Wainwright Building, St. Louis, MO	Adler & Sullivan
House of Seagram, Manhattan	Mies van der Rohe

MIT BUILDS A DREAM SOLAR HOUSE

MIT builds a house with experimental solar heating with the heating system on the roof and the furnace some 93,000,000 miles away. The sun's rays which fall on collector plates are the only energy source for the hot water system.

MIT moves in a student family as resident observers.

The living conditions are quite comfortable and the fuel bills are zero, but MIT warns solar heating is out of the financial range of most people and at this point is strictly experimental.

100

1958

The National Price Average For A New Home Is Between $12,500 And $20,000.

The typical 1958 house is 1,250 feet. Glass walls replace picture windows, and popular styles include cape cod, cinderella, contemporary and split-level. The Japanese look, with clean lines and sliding glass walls, is popular on the West Coast, while skylights are embraced in bathrooms everywhere.

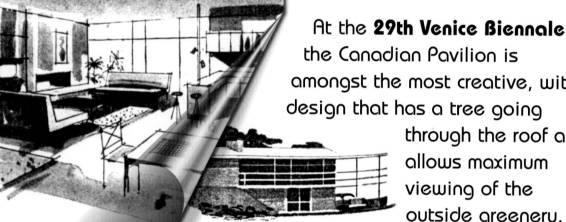

At the **29th Venice Biennale** the Canadian Pavilion is amongst the most creative, with a design that has a tree going through the roof and allows maximum viewing of the outside greenery.

The **"Balloon House"** is exhibited at the British Ideal Home Exhibition. The $1,200 house is designed by Johann Ludovici of Germany for use in the Belgian Congo. The house can easily travel on a small barge and be installed without the use of a foundation.

Great Britain's 3 millionth abode since the end of World War II is built.

CUSHIONS AVAILABLE IN *Airfoam* BY GOOD/YEAR

Furniture design patent pending

Certified...
BEST QUALITY
BUY STYLE
COMFORT

TRADE MARK

Be confident with KROEHLER

Presenting the SMARTSET '59 GROUP...

Be confident of quality and comfort! When you choose Kroehler furniture, you buy for the years ahead. Lasting satisfaction is assured by the vital "Hidden Qualities" you get only with Kroehler furniture! It is scientifically tested for truly comfortable living. Feel the comforting difference! See what solid comfort really means!

Be confident of styling and value! Designed to be admired, Kroehler furniture will stay in style with the passing years. Designed, too, to be "friendly" with your present furniture. From *every* point of view, you get more for your money when you look for the brand name of Kroehler, world's largest furniture manufacturer.

Sectional sofa in bouclé textured fabric. Choice of either end or curved corner section, $95 each . . . with Airfoam cushions, $110 each. Armless center section, $59.50 . . . with Airfoam cushions, $69.50. Pillow-back lounge chair in textured Nylon friezé, with Airfoam seat and back cushions, $119.50. Round cocktail table, $39.50. End table, $29.50. Dining table, $74.50. Side chairs, $17.50 each. Buffet, $99.50. Open hutch china cabinet, $149.50. Prices slightly higher in some areas. Convenient terms offered by most Kroehler dealers. Dining and bedroom furniture and living room tables shown in Saddle Walnut Finish. Also available in Pongee Walnut Finish. *See your Kroehler dealer now!*

KROEHLER MFG. CO., General Offices: Naperville, Illinois. In Canada: Stratford, Ontario

Sofa in textured Nylon friezé, $150...with Airfoam cushions, $175. Matching chair, $79.50...with Airfoam cushions, $89.50.

Relaxer Chair in leather-like upholstery and textured bouclé . . . seat cushioned with foam rubber, $99.50. Electric massage motor available at extra cost.

Double dresser, mirror and bookcase bed, complete, $189.50. Night table, $39.50. Chest (not shown) $69.50.

Big enough for the whole neighborhood, your 22-foot Above-Ground Pool only costs $600 and can be built without professional help. As popularity grows, costs have come down for In-The-Ground Pools, with prices ranging from $1,500-$4,000.

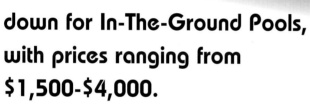

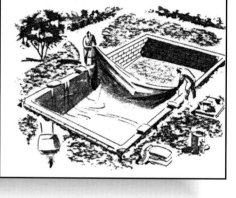

Living is so much

Even if your present house is only 5 years old, you'll find remarkable advances in the homes now being built

Wouldn't you love a home with a really well-planned kitchen—more cabinet space, more counter space, more work-saving appliances?

. . . a home with a family room off the kitchen so you can keep an eye on the kids while they play?

. . . a home that's thoroughly insulated to stay snug and warm in winter, comfortably cool all summer?

. . . a home with an extra bathroom near the children's bedroom . . . big closets and plenty of them . . . concealed baseboard or radiant-type heating systems that save space, don't catch dust?

Today's progressive builders are offering just that kind of home—in beautiful communities, planned so that houses are set far enough apart for privacy . . . and close enough for congenial living. They're sunnier, roomier, *happier* homes, built with Gold Bond's fine family of building products.

On the outside of many of these homes, you'll find beautiful Gold Bond Asbestos Siding. Inside the walls, Gold Bond Twinsulation®. It keeps the house comfortable all year 'round—and cuts fuel bills, too. Inner walls are substantially made of Gold Bond Lath and Plaster (or you may prefer Gold Bond Gypsum Wallboard). Many rooms have Gold Bond® Acoustical Ceilings—beautiful ceilings that soak up noise, make living pleasantly quieter. Walls are finished with Gold Bond Velvet—the latex paint you can sponge clean.

Can you afford such a home? If you now rent, you can buy your "dream home" in monthly installments that will probably run no more than your present rent. And under the new package mortgages, you may be able to include many extras—like a dishwasher, food-waste disposer, freezer, washer and dryer.

Why not see some of these beautiful new homes for yourself? No better time than this very week end!

National Gypsum Company · Buffalo 2, New York

BUY A NEW HOME—YOUR BEST INVESTMENT

1958

New Ideas For Bathrooms

Include A Toilet Hung From The Wall, One Faucet For Both Hot And Cold Water, Twin Washbasins And Heated Towel Holders.

Prefabricated Kitchens Include An Overhead Refrigerator, Food Warming Area, Wall Oven And An Intercom System.

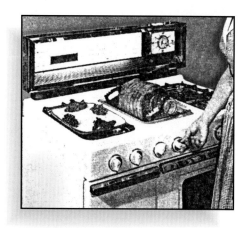

Kitchen appliances keep getting better. Some of this year's best:

- Split-level ovens, that can cook two things in two compartments at the same time.

- Oven cleaning is simple with releasable door latches that allow the door to drop down so you can get to the back with ease.

- Refrigerators contain swiveling shelves for access to food in the back.

A Well Decorated House

Is An International House, With Pieces From Around The World. Swedish Crystal, Philippine Lanterns, Indian Door Pulls, French Chairs And Henri Matisse Designed Fabric Are Showing Up In American Homes Everywhere.

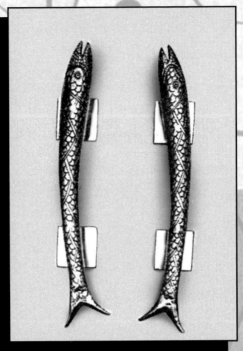

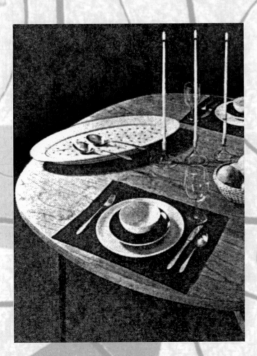

Introducing the "Linear Look"...

OLDSMOBILE

So totally new...so typically Olds!

Ninety-Eight Holiday SceniCoupe—features new heat-resistant rear window, combining cool comfort with maximum visibility. Sceni-Coupe styling also available in Dynamic 88 and Super 88 Series.

for '59

Here you see the start of a new styling cycle! Sweeping expanses of glass enhance Oldsmobile's new inner spaciousness. For in every '59 Olds there's *new roominess*...here, there, everywhere... from leg room to luggage space! New Rocket Engines, too, newly engineered for quietness, smoothness *and economy*! And everywhere you look on *every* '59 Olds you'll find the *added values* you asked for . . . from new Magic-Mirror Finishes to safety-cooled Air-Scoop Brakes on *all four* wheels. See the quality leader of the medium price class—the exciting '59 Oldsmobile!

OLDSMOBILE DIVISION, GENERAL MOTORS CORPORATION

Super 88 Holiday SportSedan—full family size with 4-door convenience plus the flair of a sports car. Also available in the Dynamic 88 (right rear) and Ninety-Eight Series.

Discover the <u>added</u> <u>values</u> in OLDSmobility...

at your local quality dealer's!

Stamford, Connecticut's New First Presbyterian Church, Shaped like A Fish, Is Dedicated.

Pre-Columbian Art Influences Upholstery Patterns.

WHAT A YEAR IT WAS!

Entertainment 1958

Top Box Office *Stars*

Brigitte Bardot
Marlon Brando
Yul Brynner
Glenn Ford
William Holden
Rock Hudson
Jerry Lewis
Frank Sinatra
James Stewart
Elizabeth Taylor

Stars *Of Tomorrow*

Red Buttons
Anthony Franciosa
Andy Griffith
Burl Ives
Hope Lange
Mike Shaughnessy
Russ Tamblyn
Diane Varsi

Photoplay Magazine Gold Medal Awards

Steve Allen presents award to **Deborah Kerr** for "most popular actress of 1957" which is based on votes of moviegoers all over the nation.

Rock Hudson beams as he scores a repeat winning "most popular actor" again and receives his trophy from **Hedda Hopper**.

FILM FAVORITES

A Tale Of Two Cities

A Night To Remember

Ashes And Diamonds

Andy Hardy Comes Home

Attack Of The 50 Foot Woman

Auntie Mame

THE BARBARIAN AND THE GEISHA

Bell, Book And Candle

The Big Country

Bonjour Tristesse

The Brothers Karamazov

THE BUCCANEER

Calypso

Cat On A Hot Tin Roof

COWBOY

CURSE OF THE DEMON

DAMN YANKEES

The Defiant Ones

DRACULA

The Fly

FOLIES BERGERE

The Geisha Boy

Gigi

The Goddess

THE HORSE'S MOUTH

High School Confidential

Indiscreet

In Love And War

The Inn Of The Sixth Happiness

KING CREOLE

WHAT A YEAR IT WAS!

1958

I WANT TO LIVE!
The Last Hurrah
Lonelyhearts
The Long, Hot Summer
LOOK BACK IN ANGER
The Magician
Me And The Colonel
Mon Oncle
Marjorie Morningstar
The Naked And The Dead
The Old Man And The Sea
The Quiet American
No Time For Sergeants
Run Silent, Run Deep
SEPARATE TABLES
The Seven Hills Of Rome
The Seventh Voyage Of Sinbad
Some Came Running
South Pacific
Tarzan's Fight For Life
TEN NORTH FREDERICK
Terror From The Year 5000
Thunder Road
Touch Of Evil
Uncle Vanya
VERTIGO
THE VIKINGS
Witness For The Prosecution
The Young Lions

1958

Academy Awards Presentation Ceremony *At The* Pantages Theatre

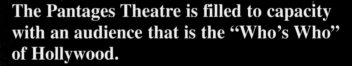

The Pantages Theatre is filled to capacity with an audience that is the "Who's Who" of Hollywood.

Marge and **Gower Champion** and **Debbie Reynolds** among the stars attending the annual Academy Awards.

Lana Turner presents the award for Best Supporting Actor to **Red Buttons** for his role in "Sayonara."

114

Anthony Quinn makes the presentation to Japan's **Miyoshi Umeki** for Best Supporting Actress for her role opposite Mr. Buttons in "Sayonara."

Producer **Sam Spiegel** makes acceptance speech after receiving his Oscar from **Gary Cooper** for "The Bridge On The River Kwai."

Accepting the award for Best Actor awarded to **Alec Guinness** is **Jean Simmons** presented by fellow Englishman **Cary Grant** for Guinness' work in "The Bridge On The River Kwai."

And the Best Actress award presented by **John Wayne** goes to **Joanne Woodward** for her brilliant work in "The Three Faces Of Eve."

An example of Magnavox value —*The Magnasonic 297* high fidelity phonograph with 10 watt amplifier, four speakers including 15″ bass, precision changer with Diamond Pick-up. Your choice of several beautiful finishes. In mahogany, now only $179.50.

An innovation in beauty and functional design. The Continental *is the only high fidelity FM-AM radio-phonograph with 25 watt dual-channel amplifier, 15″ bass and treble exponential horn speakers. Precision changer with Diamond Pick-up. Select from a variety of styles and fine woods. In mahogany, $389.50.*

Let Magnavox High Fidelity fill your home
with the glow of beautiful music

Elegance in traditional fine furniture is yours to enjoy with this beautiful 18th Century high fidelity FM-AM radio-phonograph. *The Wedgewood,* in genuine mahogany, $398.50.

High Fidelity in TV too. *The High Fidelity Theatre,* with 332 sq. in. Chromatic TV, superb FM-AM radio, precision record changer, Diamond Pickup, 4 speakers, 20 watt amplifier. Magnavox TV is priced from $169.90.

Music truly becomes magic when Magnavox sets it free. *All* of the world's great symphonies, ballads and popular dance tunes are perfectly re-created with tonal beauty and purity that will amaze and delight you.

Magnificent Magnavox high fidelity instruments are the finest you can buy, combining superior engineering and features not found in brands that cost twice as much. And only Magnavox fine furniture offers you so many innovations in beauty and functional design. You'll enjoy the convenience of stainproof glass panels that glide open to the record changer without disturbing your appointments.

Prove to yourself that Magnavox is the finest . . . and the best buy on *any* basis of comparison. It costs you less than you may think. Magnavox is sold direct only to fine stores in your community; carefully selected for their integrity and ability to serve you better. Select from 44 beautiful styles, in all price ranges, at your Magnavox dealers.

magnificent

Magnavox

high fidelity television • radio-phonographs
Precision electronics for industry and our Government

THE MAGNAVOX COMPANY, FORT WAYNE, INDIANA
Prices and specifications subject to change without notice

The Academy Awards For 1958

(For 1957 Films)

"And The Winner Is..."

BEST PICTURE
The Bridge On The River Kwai

BEST ACTOR
ALEC GUINNESS, *The Bridge On The River Kwai*

BEST ACTRESS
JOANNE WOODWARD, *The Three Faces Of Eve*

BEST DIRECTOR
DAVID LEAN, *The Bridge On The River Kwai*

BEST SUPPORTING ACTOR
RED BUTTONS, *Sayonara*

BEST SUPPORTING ACTRESS
MIYOSHI UMEKI, *Sayonara*

BEST SONG
"ALL THE WAY," *The Joker Is Wild*

1958 Favorites *(Oscars Presented In 1959)*

BEST PICTURE
Gigi

BEST ACTOR
DAVID NIVEN, *Separate Tables*

BEST ACTRESS
SUSAN HAYWARD, *I Want To Live!*

BEST DIRECTOR
VINCENTE MINNELLI,
Gigi

BEST SUPPORTING ACTOR
BURL IVES,
The Big Country

BEST SUPPORTING ACTRESS
WENDY HILLER, *Separate Tables*

BEST SONG
"GIGI," *Gigi*

1958

Filming begins on M-G-M's

The Ten Commandments

with an estimated budget of $8.5 to $15 million and shooting time of up to six months vs. the usual 60 days for the average movie.

HOLLYWOOD PRODUCERS: ARE YOU PAYING ATTENTION?

In a poll taken on the habits of the movie-going public, it is revealed that the number one reason for seeing a film is the story and not the star.

And That's Not All Folks

The Movie Cartoon Celebrates Its 50th Year

ONE, TWO, THREE KICK

New York's famed Radio City Music Hall celebrates its 25th year with the showing of "Sayonara" starring Marlon Brando.

FAMOUS BIRTHS

Angela Bassett
Alec Baldwin
Annette Benning
Tim Burton
Jamie Lee Curtis

Diner

Kevin Bacon
Tim Daly
Steve Guttenberg

Holly Hunter
Jennifer Jason Leigh
Andie MacDowell
Mary Elizabeth Mastrantonio
Barry Miller
Gary Oldman
Miranda Richardson
Tim Robbins

Passings

Producer **Louis B. Mayer**, founder of the Academy Of Motion Picture Arts And Sciences and co-founder of MGM, dies at age 72.

One of the first movie moguls, **Harry Cohn**, originator of Columbia studios, producer and movie star mentor dies at age 66.

Oscar-winning star of "A Double Life," British born **Ronald Colman**, who played Shakespearean actors, rogues and perfect gentlemen, dies at age 67.

British screen and stage star **Robert Donat**, Best Actor Academy Award winner in 1939 for his role in "Goodbye, Mr. Chips," dies in London at age 53.

Swashbuckling movie star beloved by legions of loyal fans, **Tyrone Power** dies on location in Spain of a heart attack suffered on the set of "Queen of Sheba," at age 44.

"King Solomon's Mines" producer **Sam Zimbalist** dies from a heart attack at age 51 on the set of his latest film "Ben Hur."

44-year movie producer veteran **Jessy Lasky**, one of the creators of the first full-length movie and a founding member of Hollywood, dies at age 77.

MUSIC

1958 POPULAR SONGS

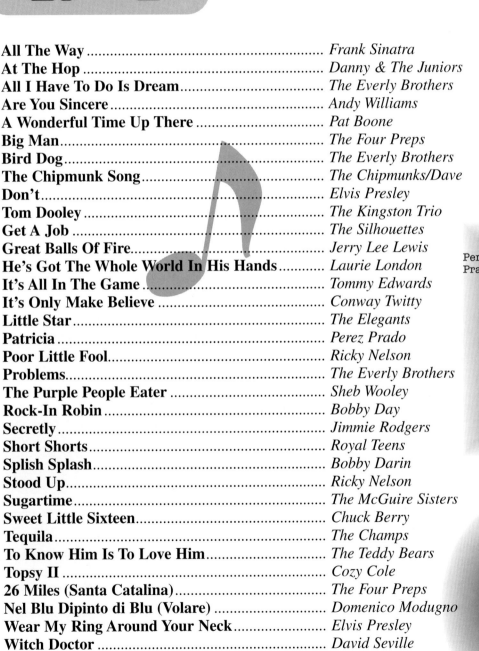

All The Way	*Frank Sinatra*
At The Hop	*Danny & The Juniors*
All I Have To Do Is Dream	*The Everly Brothers*
Are You Sincere	*Andy Williams*
A Wonderful Time Up There	*Pat Boone*
Big Man	*The Four Preps*
Bird Dog	*The Everly Brothers*
The Chipmunk Song	*The Chipmunks/Dave*
Don't	*Elvis Presley*
Tom Dooley	*The Kingston Trio*
Get A Job	*The Silhouettes*
Great Balls Of Fire	*Jerry Lee Lewis*
He's Got The Whole World In His Hands	*Laurie London*
It's All In The Game	*Tommy Edwards*
It's Only Make Believe	*Conway Twitty*
Little Star	*The Elegants*
Patricia	*Perez Prado*
Poor Little Fool	*Ricky Nelson*
Problems	*The Everly Brothers*
The Purple People Eater	*Sheb Wooley*
Rock-In Robin	*Bobby Day*
Secretly	*Jimmie Rodgers*
Short Shorts	*Royal Teens*
Splish Splash	*Bobby Darin*
Stood Up	*Ricky Nelson*
Sugartime	*The McGuire Sisters*
Sweet Little Sixteen	*Chuck Berry*
Tequila	*The Champs*
To Know Him Is To Love Him	*The Teddy Bears*
Topsy II	*Cozy Cole*
26 Miles (Santa Catalina)	*The Four Preps*
Nel Blu Dipinto di Blu (Volare)	*Domenico Modugno*
Wear My Ring Around Your Neck	*Elvis Presley*
Witch Doctor	*David Seville*
Yakety Yak	*The Coasters*

Chuck Berry

Perez Prado

Ricky Nelson

PHILCO CREATES WORLD'S FIRST SEPARATE SCREEN TV SET!

Keep the set beside your chair...

MODEL 4710L   21-INCH OVERALL DIAGONAL MEASUREMENT SCREEN

...put the picture anywhere!

ANNOUNCING THE NEW PHILCO

Predicta Tandem

Philco builds chassis and sound system into a table . . . makes picture tube separate and portable!

Philco brings you another spectacular advance in the science of television! Now the picture tube is completely freed from the chassis . . . can be placed anywhere in the room . . . even carried to another room!

This revolutionary new Philco Predicta Tandem was made possible by Philco scientists who developed the new "S-F" (Semi-Flat) picture tube. Ordinary tubes would have been far too bulky and cumbersome. A flexible 25-ft. cord connects the powerful chassis with the big, bright picture tube.

The set itself, with *all its controls and the speaker system,* is built into an elegant modern end table. Philco's full, rich sound is right at your elbow, always conversation-clear. You can put the picture on a wall shelf, where a roomful of people can enjoy it, or place it up close to your chair for personal viewing.

This tomorrow-new television is at your Philco dealer's now. You can own Predicta Tandem in blond wood, as shown, for $339.95, and in mahogany finish for only **$329.95.**

SPECIFICATIONS SUBJECT TO CHANGE WITHOUT NOTICE. PRICES SLIGHTLY HIGHER SOUTH AND WEST. UHF SLIGHTLY HIGHER.

LOOK AHEAD... *and you'll choose*

TV today from the world of tomorrow!

120

Hit Singles

CATCH A FALLING STAR
Perry Como

TWILIGHT TIME
Platters

LOLLIPOP
Chordettes

WHO'S SORRY NOW?
Connie Francis

TEA FOR TWO CHA CHA
Tommy Dorsey

FEVER
Peggy Lee

HARD-HEADED WOMAN
Elvis Presley

BALLAD OF A TEENAGE QUEEN
Johnny Cash

WHAT A YEAR IT WAS!

Top Albums

RICKY
Ricky Nelson

COME FLY WITH ME
Frank Sinatra

THE MUSIC MAN
Original Cast

SOUTH PACIFIC
Soundtrack

JOHNNY'S GREATEST HITS
Johnny Mathis

Peggy Lee

The First Annual GRAMMY AWARDS
The Winners

Record Of The Year
"Nel Blu Dipinto di Blu" (Volare)
Domenico Modugno

Song Of The Year
"Nel Blu Dipinto di Blu" (Volare)
Domenico Modugno

Album Of The Year
"The Music From Peter Gunn"
Henry Mancini

Best Vocal Performance
MALE
Perry Como
"Catch A Falling Star"
FEMALE
Ella Fitzgerald
"Ella Fitzgerald Sings The Irving Berlin Songbook"

1958

Frank Sinatra

Downbeat's Top Performers

"We are the envy of all European musicians," remarks three German jazz musicians hired to play with Benny Goodman.

Benny Goodman protege Peggy Lee's *"Is That All There Is"* skyrockets to top of charts.

Paul Desmond

COUNT BASIE	SOLOIST, BIG BAND
LES BROWN	DANCE BAND
MODERN JAZZ QUARTET	JAZZ QUARTET
OSCAR PETERSON	PIANO
SHELLEY MANNE	DRUMS
PAUL DESMOND	ALTO SAXOPHONE
TONY SCOTT	CLARINET
MILT JACKSON	VIBES
HERBIE MANN	FLUTE
ART VAN DAMME	ACCORDIAN
ELLA FITZGERALD	FEMALE VOCALIST
FRANK SINATRA	MALE VOCALIST
FOUR FRESHMEN	VOCAL GROUP

Ella Fitzgerald

The First MONTEREY JAZZ FESTIVAL Kicks Off Featuring LOUIS ARMSTRONG.

MAMBO KING PEREZ PRADO'S RECORDING OF "PATRICIA" KICKS OFF THE CHA CHA DANCE CRAZE.

WHAT A YEAR IT WAS!

FIRST TIME RECORDING ARTISTS

Frankie Avalon

Dion & The Belmonts

Duane Eddy

Connie Francis

Impressions

Kingston Trio

Little Anthony & The Imperials

Miracles

Neil Sedaka

Shirelles

Ritchie Valens

♪ Warner Bros. Records Begins Operations.

♪ Country Music Association Is First Trade Organization To Promote A Specific Genre Of Music.

♪ Teenagers Are Responsible For 70% Of Record Sales.

FAMOUS BIRTHS

Shaun Cassidy

Andy Gibb

Ice-T

Alan Jackson

Tanya Tucker

Bill Berry

R.E.M.

Michael Mills

The Artist Formerly Known As Prince

Michael Jackson

Madonna

Passings

Legendary "Father of the Blues" **W.C. Handy**, composer of songs such as "St. Louis Blues" and "Beale Street Blues," dies at age 84. Over 150,000 mourners attend his Harlem funeral procession.

Top selling blues recording artist of the 30's, **Big Bill Broonzy**, known for his earthy vocals and primal guitar work, dies at age 65.

Gladys Smith Presley, mother of the King of Rock & Roll, dies at age 42.

BOBBY DARIN'S "Splish Splash"

Sells Over 100,000 Records In Less Than 30 Days.

ELVIS PRESLEY

Completes His 19th Consecutive Recording To Sell More Than 1,000,000 Copies Establishing A New Record For Popular Music Sales.

The First Gold Record Award Is Established By Record Industry Associates Of America For A Single Selling 1 Million Copies Or An LP Achieving $1 Million In Sales.

Little Richard Gives Up Rock & Roll To Serve God After A Near Death Experience On A Plane To Australia.

Jerry Lee Lewis Cancels His English Tour After An Outraged Audience Hisses And Boos In Protest Over Marriage To His 13-Year Old Cousin Which Also Causes Him To Be Blacklisted In The United States.

George Harrison Joins the Quarrymen, a band featuring **John Lennon** and **Paul McCartney**.

New York Rock & Roll D.J. Alan Freed's Touring Show Banned By Four Cities Following Riot In Boston Area.

Classical Music

New Compositions

Poeme Electronique
Edgard Varese

Symphony No. 4
Roger Sessions

Symphony No. 2
George Rochberg

Fontana Mix
John Cage

0,0,0,0, That Shakespearian Rag
Salvatore Martirano

 GIAN-CARLO MENOTTI Launches His "Festival Of Two Worlds" In Spoleto, Italy Opening With A Performance Of Verdi's "Macbeth."

 OSCAR LEVANT Performs Shostakovich's "Piano Concerto No. 2" At The Opening Of The Los Angeles Music Festival.

 Eccentric Canadian-Born 25-Year Old Pianist GLENN GOULD One Of The Most Talked About Musicians In The World.

 Van Cliburn's recording of Tchaikovsky's "Piano Concerto No. 1 in B-Flat Minor" makes classical music history by selling 300,000 copies in first six weeks of release.

Pablo Casals appears in New York for the first time in over twenty years in honor of UN day.

After an 11-year absence, **Paul Robeson** returns to New York.

 Former **President Truman** and **Jack Benny** play with the Kansas City Philharmonic at a benefit performance.

Four American composers invited to the Soviet Union—**Roy Harris, Ulysses Kay, Peter Mennin** and **Roger Sessions**.

Vladimir Ashkenazy and **Leonid Kogan** make their musical debuts.

Leopold Stokowski begins his 50th year conducting in the U.S.

Leonard Bernstein appointed musical director of the New York Philharmonic Orchestra becoming the first native-born American to hold that position.

| PULITZER PRIZE FOR MUSIC | *Vanessa* Samuel Barber |

Debuts Around The Country

BOSTON:
Symphony No. 3
Roger Sessions

NEW YORK:
The Dragon
Deems Taylor

CLEVELAND:
Piano Concerto
Gian-Carlo Menotti

NEW ORLEANS:
Pre-Classic Suite
Paul Creston

Cincinnati:
The Wasteland Of T.S. Eliot
Henry Humphreys

Passings

One of the great 20th century names in British music, famed composer **Ralph Vaughan Williams** dies at age 85 and is buried in Westminster Abbey.

Composer of TV's "Dragnet" theme, **Walter Schumann**, conductor, composer and choral director, dies at age 44.

OPERA NEWS

- **Gian-Carlo Menotti's** Opera "MARIA GOLOVIN" Premieres At The Brussels World's Fair.

- Tempestuous Diva **Maria Callas** Receives A 10-Minute Standing Ovation After Performance At Chicago's Civic Opera House.

- **Maria Callas** Receives A 20-Minute Standing Ovation With 18 Curtain Calls After Her Riveting Performance In Verdi's "LA TRAVIATA" Before A Star-Studded Metropolitan Opera Audience.

- **Rudolf Bing**, General Manager Of New York's Metropolitan Opera, Announces The Cancellation Of Maria Callas' Contract.

- **Carlisle Floyd's** "WUTHERING HEIGHTS" Makes Debut At Santa Fe Opera.

- "ASSASSINIO NELLA CATTEDRALE" By **Ildebrando Pizzetti** Premieres At La Scala.

- **Benjamin Britten's** "NOYE'S FLUDDE" Premieres In England

Dance

Dance Premieres

✵ Americans And Poles Exchange Lessons In Rock & Roll And Native Polish Dances Following A Performance Given By The American Ballet Theatre In Warsaw.

✵ Under The Auspices Of The International Cultural Program Of The United States The New York City Ballet Dances In Japan For The First Time.

✵ Russian-Born Impresario SOL HUROK Is Given The Capezio Dance Award For Bringing Russia's Beryozka Dance Company To The United States.

Antic Meet
Choreographer: Merce Cunningham
Music: John Cage

Clytemnestra
Choreographer: Martha Graham

Night Journey
Choreographers: Martha Graham & Bertram Ross

Miss Brevis
Choreographer: Jose Limon

New York City Ballet
Stars and Stripes
Square Dance
Choreographer: George Balanchine

Ballets U.S.A.
New York Export: Op. Jazz
Choreographer: Jerome Robbins

San Francisco Ballet
Beauty And The Beast
Choreographer: Lew Christensen

WHAT A YEAR IT WAS!

An Overflow Crowd Applauds More Than 60 Times During The Spectacular Performance Given By Moscow's **Moiseyev Dance Company** In Detroit's Masonic Temple.

54-Year Old Russian Born Prima Ballerina **Alexandra Danilova** Receives The Capezio Dance Award Of $1,000 Presented To Her By Greer Garson For Service To Ballet In America.

Repatriated Dancers From The Kingdom Of Yemen On The Red Sea Tour The U.S.

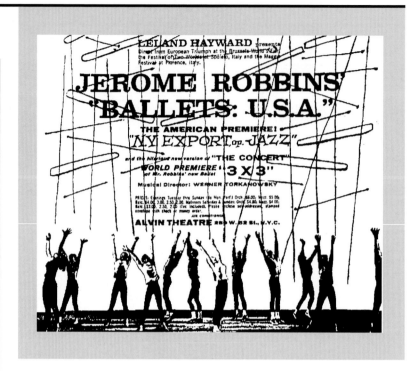

AMERICAN BALLET THEATRE

Is Formed By

ALVIN AILEY

New York Finally Gets To See A Performance Of The Much-Publicized Ballet "Le Rendez-Vous Manque" (The Broken Date) By Francoise Sagan, Directed By Roger Vadim.

Francoise Sagan

WHAT A YEAR IT WAS!

TELEVISION

OTHER T.V. FAVORITES

Steve Allen Show

Adventures Of Ozzie & Harriet

American Bandstand

Armstrong Circle Theatre

Perry Como Show

Bob Cummings Show

Desilu Playhouse

Father Knows Best

Gillette Cavalcade Of Sports

Jackie Gleason Show

Arthur Godfrey Show

Your Hit Parade

Alfred Hitchcock Presents

Alfred Hitchcock

TOP 10 TELEVISION PROGRAMS

Gunsmoke

The Danny Thomas Show

Tales Of Wells Fargo

Have Gun Will Travel

I've Got A Secret

The Life And Legend Of Wyatt Earp

General Electric Theater

The Restless Gun

December Bride

You Bet Your Life

NEW PROGRAMS

Concentration
(Hugh Downs)

Peter Gunn
(Craig Stevens)

The Lawman
(John Russell)

Naked City
(John McIntire)

Open End
(David Susskind)

The Donna Reed Show
(Donna Reed)

The Rifleman
(Chuck Connors, Johnny Crawford)

77 Sunset Strip
(Efrem Zimbalist, Jr., Edd "Kookie Byrnes)

Wanted: Dead Or Alive
(Steve McQueen)

Westinghouse Drops Sponsorship Of The Long-Running "Studio One" Opting For "The Desilu Playhouse."

RCA Laboratories Develop A Portable Tape Recorder For Recording Your Favorite Television Program Which Can Then Be Played Back Through The TV Set. It Should Be Available In About Two Years.

The Kraft TV Theatre Goes Off The Air After A Successful 11-Year Run.

Passings

Famed announcer of Edgar Bergen and Burns and Allen's radio shows and announcer on television's "Colgate Theater," **Bill Goodwin** dies at age 47.

Amos 'N' Andy star **Harry "Tim" Moore**, who played Kingfish until his retirement from the famed television show, and who began his acting career at 12, dies at age 70.

David Susskind's opinion of the American Public is that it is the best educated audience in history with an insatiable appetite for good entertainment and instruction. His opinion of television executives is slightly different calling them "irresponsible, insensitive, unwilling to take risks and guilty of callous indifference to public interest."

1958

1958 EMMY AWARDS

Presented For 1957 Programming

Jack Benny

Best Dramatic Series	**Gunsmoke**
Best Comedy Series	**The Phil Silvers Show**
Best Musical Series	**The Dinah Shore Chevy Show**
Best Dramatic Anthology	**Playhouse 90**
Best Actor in a Series	**Robert Young** *Father Knows Best*
Best Actress in a Series	**Jane Wyatt** *Father Knows Best*
Best Non-Dramatic Male Performance in a Series	**Jack Benny** *The Jack Benny Show*
Best Non-Dramatic Female Performance in a Series	**Dinah Shore** *The Dinah Shore Chevy Show*
Best News Commentary	**Edward R. Murrow** *See It Now*

OTHER T.V. FAVORITES

Lux Playhouse
The Real McCoys
The Millionaire
Arthur Murray Party
Cheyenne
The Ford Show
Red Skelton Show
Lawrence Welk's Dodge
  Dancing Party
Dinah Shore Chevy Show
Gale Storm Show
Dick Powell's
  Zane Grey Theatre
The Lineup
This Is Your Life
Name That Tune
Person To Person
People Are Funny
Phil Silvers Show
Playhouse 90
The $64,000 Question
Loretta Young Show
Lassie
What's My Line
Wagon Train
Sugarfoot
Ann Sothern Show
Dragnet
Perry Mason
Garry Moore Show
George Burns Show

FAMOUS BIRTHS

Brett Butler
Ellen DeGeneres
Jeff Foxworthy
Arsenio Hall
Eve Plumb
Kevin Sorbo

The National Association for Better Radio and Television issues a report entitled "Fifteen Reasons Why Crime-Westerns Are Not Acceptable TV Fare For Children" wherein it warns that a child's repeated exposure to brutality can result in the development of hardness and lack of compassion.

REPORTING LIVE FROM THE SKY

KTLA-TV Los Angeles kicks off on-the-spot news coverage from a roving helicopter and KABC-TV introduces "Operation Airwatch" which provides instant traffic information to Los Angeles commuters reported by newscaster Donn Reed from a helicopter piloted by Max Schumacher.

WHAT A YEAR IT WAS!

RADIO

POPULAR DAYTIME SHOWS

ARTHUR GODFREY SHOW
BREAKFAST CLUB
DOROTHY AND DICK
EDDIE ARNOLD SHOW
GALEN DRAKE
JIM BACKUS SHOW
JOHN A. GAMBLING
KATE SMITH SHOW
LUNCHEON AT SARDI'S
MARTIN BLOCK'S
    MAKE BELIEVE BALLROOM
NEWS: TEX ANTOINE
PETER LIND HAYES AND
    MARY HEALY

POPULAR EVENING SHOWS

AMOS 'N' ANDY
ANSWER PLEASE WITH
    WALTER CRONKITE
EDWARD R. MURROW
FACE THE NATION
GABRIEL HEATTER
GUNSMOKE
JACK BENNY SHOW
JOHN WINGATE
LOWELL THOMAS SHOW
MEET THE PRESS
MERV GRIFFIN
MITCH MILLER SHOW
ROBERT Q. LEWIS SHOW
TEX AND JINX SHOW
YOU BET YOUR LIFE
    (GROUCHO MARX)

POPULAR SOAPS

HELEN TRENT
MA PERKINS
OUR GAL SUNDAY
SECOND MRS. BURTON
YOUNG DOCTOR MALONE
NORA DRAKE

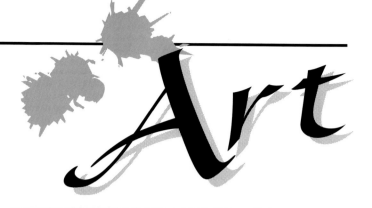

Art

The Washington DC National Gallery of Art introduces the "Lectour," an electronic guide consisting of radios and earphones that give descriptions about various works throughout the museum.

A fire at the Museum of Modern Art in New York City causes one death and destroys a Monet painting.

The Smithsonian Institution begins work on the $36 million Museum of History and Technology.

Restoration work begins as Spain's Church of San Martin at Fuentiduena is shipped in hundreds of crates to the Cloisters in New York.

Cleveland's Museum of Art opens a new $9 million wing with the latest security features including 33 surveillance cameras.

SOLD

IN ONE NIGHT AT SOTHEBY'S LONDON

Paul Cezanne	*Garcon au Gilet Rouge*	£220,000	($616,000)
Vincent Van Gogh	*Public Gardens At Arles*	£132,000	($369,600)
Edouard Manet	*La Rue de Berne*	£113,000	($316,400)
Auguste Renoir	*La Pensee*	£72,000	($201,600)

The Jewelry From The Estate Of Aimee S. Guggenheim Fetches $348,935 At A New York Auction House.

The New American Painting show travels to Europe to exhibit Abstract-Expressionism. **Arshile Gorky, Grace Hartigan, Willem de Kooning, Robert Motherwell, Jackson Pollock** and **Franz Kline** are among the represented artists.

France's **Georges Braques** receives a 20 million lire ($32,000) prize from the Rome Academy of Fine Arts.

Pablo Picasso's 80-square meter mural is unveiled at the UNESCO building in Paris. An **Alexander Calder** mobile, **Henry Moore** sculpture and **Joan Miro** frieze also adorn the complex.

The United Nations Art Club annual Unicef benefit includes paintings by **Xavier Cugat**, **Cornelia Otis Skinner** and **Elsa Maxwell**.

36 nations attend the 29th Venice Biennale. An exhibit of international artists under 40 at the Palazzo Centrale shows current trends in painting and sculpture.

150 Pablo Picasso ceramics are displayed at La Maison de la Pensee in Paris.

Paris' Bibliotheque Nationale and Amsterdam's Rijksmuseum celebrate their 150th anniversaries.

RIJKSMUSEUM

132

New York Shows

MAILLOL
Nude

Ruth Asawa
William Baziotes
Georges Braques
John Cage
Alexander Calder
Marc Chagall
Jean Cocteau
Salvador Dali
Richard Diebenkorn
Lyonel Feininger
Juan Gris
Philip Guston
Childe Hassam
Paul Klee
Aristide Maillol
Joan Miro
Giorgio Morandi
Robert de Niro
Georgia O'Keeffe
Pablo Picasso
Jackson Pollock
Mark Rothko
Georges Rouault
George Segal
Georges Seurat
The Utrillo Family
Max Weber
Andrew Wyeth

KLEE
Figure

NEO-DADAISM Comes To MANHATTAN

The anti-art sentiment of the Dada movement seems to be alive in several young American artists. **Alan Kaprow's** all-encompassing exhibit brings the viewers into his work; **Robert Rauschenberg** hangs a colorfully painted bed and quilt on the wall; and **Jasper Johns** paints what he likes, most notably flags. All three artists, 32 and under, are concerned with making art they like, and do not worry about public reaction.

Manhattan's **Wildenstein Gallery** exhibits paintings by **Auguste Renoir** along with his plaques commemorating fellow artists such as **Cezanne**, **Delacroix**, **Monet** and **Rodin**.

NOTEWORTHY WORKS

• • • • • *painting* • • • • •

Robert Motherwell	*Iberia, No. 18*
Jasper Johns	*Three Flags*
Willem de Kooning	*Woman And Bicycle*
Mark Rothko	*Four Darks On Red*

• • • • • *sculpture* • • • • •

Reuben Nakian	*The Rape Of Lucrece*

major Edgar Degas *show mounted at* Los Angeles County Museum.

A Norman Rockwell Illustration Graces The Cover Of Post Magazine For The 301st Time.

At Madison Square Garden "Art: USA '58" Displays 1500 Works.

Joan Miro's mural *"Night and Day"* wins top prize from the Guggenheim International Awards.

The Carnegie International Exhibition awards painter **Jasper Johns** an undisclosed sum to "foster good will through the arts."

FAMOUS BIRTH

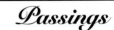

KEITH HARING

Passings

Modern artist **Georges Rouault**, member of the French Expressionist school, whose paintings, often of Jesus, are characterized by black outlines and vivid colors, dies at age 86.

French landscape painter **Maurice de Vlaminck**, co-founder of the school of Chatou, member of the Fauvist school of painting, dies at age 82.

Photographer **Edward Weston**, contemporary of Alfred Stieglitz and Ansel Adams, who never used artificial light in his pictures and had over 100 exhibits of his work, dies at age 71.

WHAT A YEAR IT WAS!

1958

books

Robert Graves
5 PENS IN HAND

E. E. Cummings
95 POEMS

Lawrence Ferlinghetti
A CONEY ISLAND OF THE MIND

Frank Lloyd Wright
A TESTAMENT

Winston S. Churchill
A HISTORY OF THE ENGLISH SPEAKING PEOPLES, VOL. 4: THE GREAT DEMOCRACIES

J. K. Galbraith
THE AFFLUENT SOCIETY

Thor Heyerdahl
AKU-AKU

Edmund Wilson
THE AMERICAN EARTHQUAKE

Patrick Dennis
AROUND THE WORLD WITH AUNTIE MAME

Lawrence Durrell
BALTHAZAR
BITTER LEMONS

Truman Capote
BREAKFAST AT TIFFANY'S

Dr. Suess
CAT IN THE HAT COMES BACK
YERTLE THE TURTLE & OTHER STORIES

Mazo de la Roche
CENTENARY AT JALNA

Abigail Van Buren
DEAR ABBY

Boris Pasternak
DOCTOR ZHIVAGO

Lawrence Durrell

Jerome Weidman
THE ENEMY CAMP

T. S. Eliot
THE ELDER STATESMAN

Leon Uris
EXODUS

W. A. Swanberg
FIRST BLOOD: THE STORY OF FORT SUMTER

Rumer Godden
THE GREENGAGE SUMMER

Edna Ferber
ICE PALACE

John Gunther
INSIDE RUSSIA TODAY

Mary Renault
THE KING MUST DIE

Roger Vailland
THE LAW

Franz Kafka
LETTERS 1902-1924

Nathan Leopold
LIFE PLUS 99 YEARS

Vladimir Nabokov
LOLITA

Richard Wright
THE LONG DREAM

Laurens Van Der Post
THE LOST WORLD OF THE KALAHARI

J. Edgar Hoover
MASTERS OF DECEIT

H. R. Trevor-Roper
MEN AND EVENTS

Angus Wilson
THE MIDDLE AGE OF MRS. ELIOT

Richard Sedgewick West, Jr.
MR. LINCOLN'S NAVY

J. Christopher Herold
MISTRESS TO AN AGE: A LIFE OF MADAME DE STAEL

> The First National Library Week Is Held Across The Country. President Eisenhower Lends His Support.

Popular American Authors Under 40 Years Old

Norman Mailer

J.D. Salinger

Gore Vidal

Truman Capote

William Styron

Jack Kerouac

A CONEY ISLAND OF THE MIND POEMS BY LAWRENCE FERLINGHETTI

Theodore H. White
The Mountain Road

Linus Pauling
No More War

A. J. Cronin
Northern Light

Eleanor Roosevelt
On My Own

Harry Golden
Only In America

Cyril N. Parkinson
Parkinson's Law

William Carlos Williams
Paterson (Book Five)

Graham Greene
The Potting Shed

David Douglas Duncan
The Private World Of Pablo Picasso

Nevil Shute
The Rainbow And The Rose

Alan Moorehead
The Russian Revolution

Carl Sandburg
The Sandburg Range

Elick Moll
Seidman And Son

James Jones
Some Came Running

Martin Luther King, Jr.
Stride Toward Freedom

Jack Kerouac
The Subterraneans
The Dharma Bums

Alice Ekert-Rotholz
The Time Of The Dragons

William Lederer &
Eugene Burdick
The Ugly American

Carl Jung
The Undiscovered Self

Mary McMinnies
The Visitors

Nancy Mitford
Voltaire In Love

Anya Seton
The Winthrop Woman

Dorothy Canfield Fisher, author of novels depicting New England life, Book-Of-The-Month Club founding board member, women's rights champion and member of the National Institute of Arts and Letters, dies at age 79.

Author **Mary Roberts Rinehart** wrote for more than 40 years, put the first American mystery on the best-seller list and used the same pen for more than two decades, dies at age 82.

Random House editor of Nobel Prize-winning tomes by William Faulkner and Eugene O'Neill, **Saxe Commins** dies at age 66.

Artist **Frank Willard**, whose "Moon Mullins" comic strip has become one of the country's most popular and is read in over 250 North American papers, dies at age 64.

Best-selling author **Betty MacDonald** dies at age 49.

PRIZES

NOBEL

Literature:

Boris Pasternak (USSR)

The Doctor Zhivago author turns down the prize after Russian government puts pressure on him.

PULITZER

Letters:

James Agee
A Death In The Family

Poetry:

Robert Penn Warren
Promises: Poems 1954-1956

History:

Bray Hammond
Banks And Politics In America—From The Revolution To The Civil War

Journalism:

Arkansas Gazette, Little Rock

Reporting:

George Beveridge
Evening Star, Washington DC

Editorial Cartooning:

Bruce M. Shanks
Buffalo Evening News

Poetry Society of America Awards

Robert Frost Gold Medal
Kenneth Rexroth
Shelley Memorial Award

ON BROADWAY

CLASSICS
AND
REVIVALS
RETURN TO
ON &
OFF~
BROADWAY
THEATRES

Eric
Portman
and
Kim
Stanley
in
**A TOUCH
OF THE
POET**

ANOTHER OPENING, ANOTHER NIGHT

Juanita Hall in FLOWER DRUM SONG

John Kerr and June Havoc in THE INFERNAL MACHINE

Pulitzer Prize for Drama

Ketti Frings
LOOK HOMEWARD, ANGEL

New York Drama Critics' Circle Award

Best Play

Ketti Frings
LOOK HOMEWARD, ANGEL

Best Musical

Meredith Wilson
THE MUSIC MAN

Best Foreign Play

John Osborne
LOOK BACK IN ANGER

PASSINGS

Famed Broadway lyricist of such successful musicals as "Annie Get Your Gun," **HERBERT FIELDS** dies in New York at age 60.

"The New Yorker" writer and drama critic **WALCOTT GIBBS**, author of his own Broadway success, "Season In The Sun," dies at age 56.

WHAT'S ON BROADWAY

Ages Of Man
(Shakespeare Scenes & Sonnets)
John Gielgud

A Touch Of The Poet
(Eugene O'Neill)
Kim Stanley, Eric Portman,
Helen Hayes, Betty Field

The Cold Wind And The Warm
(S.N. Behrman)
Eli Wallach, Maureen Stapleton

The Disenchanted
(Bud Schulberg & Harvey Breit)
Rosemary Harris, George Grizzard,
Jason Robards, Jr.

The Entertainer
(John Osborne)
Laurence Olivier, Joan Plowright

Epitaph For George Dillon
(John Osborne &
Anthony Creighton)
Eileen Herlie, Robert Stephens

Flower Drum Song
(Richard Rodgers, Oscar
Hammerstein & Joseph Fields)
Pat Suzuki, Juanita Hall, Larry Blyden,
Miyoshi Umeki

J. P.
(Archibald MacLeish)
Pat Hingle, Christopher Plummer,
Raymond Massey

✫

The Marriage-Go-Round
(Leslie Stevens)
Charles Boyer, Claudette Colbert

✫

A Party With Betty Comden
And Adolph Green
Betty Comden, Adolph Green

✫

The Pleasure Of His Company
(Samuel Taylor)
Cyril Ritchard, Cornelia Otis Skinner

✫

La Plume De Ma Tante
(Gerard Calvi)
Robert Dhery, Colette Brosset

✫

Sunrise At Campobello
(Dory Schary)
Ralph Bellamy

✫

Two For The Seesaw
(William Gibson)
Henry Fonda, Anne Bancroft

✫

The World Of Suzie Wong
(Paul Osborn)
France Nuyen, William Shatner

Eli Wallach and Morris Carnovsky
in
THE COLD WIND AND THE WARM

OTHER NOTABLE PLAYS

A Taste Of Honey
(Shelagh Delaney)

✫

A Raisin In The Sun
(Lorraine Hansberry)

✫

The Birthday Party
(Harold Pinter)

TONY AWARDS

OUTSTANDING ACHIEVEMENTS

PLAY	**Sunrise At Campobello** Dory Schary
MUSICAL	**The Music Man** Meredith Wilson
ACTOR (DRAMA)	**Ralph Bellamy** Sunrise At Campobello
ACTRESS (DRAMA)	**Helen Hayes** Time Remembered
ACTOR (MUSICAL)	**Robert Preston** The Music Man
ACTRESS (MUSICAL)	**Thelma Ritter & Gwen Verdon** New Girl In Town
DIRECTOR (DRAMA)	**Vincent J. Donehue** Sunrise At Campobello
DIRECTOR (MUSICAL)	**Herbert Greene** The Music Man
DIRECTOR (DANCE)	**Jerome Robbins** West Side Story

CLASSICS AND REVIVALS

Blood Wedding
(Garcia Lorca)

✶

The Chairs & The Lesson
(Eugene Ionesco)

✶

Endgame
(Samuel Beckett)

✶

Family Reunion
(T. S. Eliot)

✶

Garden District
(Tennessee Williams)

✶

Hamlet, Twelfth Night
(William Shakespeare)

✶

The Infernal Machine
(Jean Cocteau)

✶

Ivanov
(Anton Chekhov)

✶

The Quare Fellow
(Brendan Behan)

✶

Ulysses In Nighttown
(Oliver Saylor)

DISASTERS

BRITAIN MOURNS THE LOSS OF ITS SOCCER CHAMPIONS

The Manchester United Soccer Team was on its way back from Belgrade after tying Yugoslavia in the European Championship Competition.

This twisted wreckage is all that's left of the British airliner which crashed near Munich slightly after takeoff killing the entire team who were national heroes. A shocking disaster and terrible blow to Great Britain.

FIRES

Two people die and flames damage the Manhattan Bridge when the Swedish freighter "Nebraska" rams a U.S. oil tanker in New York's East River.

Fire Sweeps Chicago Parochial School Killing 95.

In Bogota, Colombia Fire Ravages Department Store Killing 83 Shoppers.

Two people die with property damage estimated in excess of $15,000,000 in a two-day oil refinery fire in Long Beach California.

420 People Die In Car Accidents Over Labor Day Weekend.

99 PEOPLE DIE IN ROYAL DUTCH AIRLINES CRASH OFF THE COAST OF IRELAND.

ONE OF FOUR U.S. STRATEGIC AIR COMMAND JET TANKERS ATTEMPTING TO SET NEW SPEED RECORDS FOR NON-STOP ROUND TRIP FLIGHT TO LONDON CRASHES NEAR WESTOVER AIR FORCE BASE KILLING 15 PEOPLE.

TRAINS

128 People Die In Train Wreck In Rio de Janeiro, Brazil.

50 people die as train bound from Bay Head, New Jersey to Jersey City fails to stop at an open drawbridge plunging into 35 feet of water.

SCHOOL BUS

A school bus plunges into the Big Sandy River near Prestonburg, Kentucky drowning 27 children and bus driver.

In the heavily fogged-in harbor in Newport, Rhode Island, tanker "Gulfoil" rams oil-ladened tanker "S. E. Graham" resulting in 16 dead, 34 crew injuries and 2 people unaccounted for.

170 People Die In Snowstorms That Sweep The East Coast From Virginia To Maine.

13 people die with property damage estimated at $12,000,000 as floods hit Northern California.

6-Week Heat Wave Kills 651 People In Northern And Central India.

Over 1,000 people die as Japan's worst typhoon in 25 years hits central Japan with winds up to 160 miles per hour and torrential rains that cause massive flooding.

WHAT A YEAR IT WAS!

The Sack Dress

The Sack Dress, also known as the Chemise, continues to be both controversial and one of the best selling dresses in the world. Everyone has a strong opinion about it. Fashion watcher Billy Graham tells a San Francisco audience that he is in favor of the Sack Dress, while former Secretary of State Dean Acheson believes women who wear it look no better than a sack of potatoes. Actresses Gina Lollobrigida and Rhonda Fleming refuse to wear the dress, while Marilyn Monroe and Loretta Young embrace the look. An opinion poll shows men dislike the Sack 9 to 1.

Coco Chanel

Sacks The Sack In Her Fall Line And Shows Clothes That Profile A Woman's Natural Curves.

Waistlines Rise As The Empire Dress, Coat And Suit Make A Comeback

CRUISEWEAR FOR CRUISING

A one-piece polka dot bathing suit made of a miracle fiber has a collar should a chill set in.

The popular bikini in a stripe knit material with naughty deep cut-outs over the hip.

This two-piece ensemble made of trim, crisp, wash 'n' wear no-iron fabrics is perfect for sports performed out of the water

Shuffleboard becomes even more fun with these fashionable outfits made from no-iron fabrics.

French photographers and models get ready to shoot the latest Spring Collection from designer Guy Laroche.

French Fashion Photographers Shoot The Spring Collection

In a busy world of bright new fabrics and "tres chic" styles there is a great responsibility for what is unveiled will influence millions of women around the world.

A beautiful coat and dress ensemble.

This flowing cocktail dress should wind up in the wardrobes of style-conscious women from Paris to Rome to New York.

The look is definitely more feminine and away from "The Sack." (Above and Left)

1958

BRUSSELS WORLD'S FAIR

THE NEVER-ENDING FASHION SHOW IN THE AMERICAN PAVILION SECTION OF THE BRUSSELS WORLD'S FAIR DISPLAYS REAL-LIFE AMERICAN CLOTHES SUCH AS JEANS, DRESSES WORN FOR ERRANDS AND SPORTSWEAR. EUROPEAN MODELS ARE GIVEN AN AMERICAN MAKE-OVER FOR AUTHENTICITY.

N.Y.

New York University Presents A Fashion Show Of Creative Designs For The Handicapped.

She's Got Legs – She Knows How To Use Them

Skirts are a whopping 2 inches shorter than last year, but please, no knees. If you don't show any legs at all, you'll look hopelessly old-fashioned. Later in the year French designers Balenciaga and Givenchy are among the many who bring the hemlines back above the knees, much to the relief of leg fans everywhere.

ALI BABA, MAKE ME LOOK GLAMOUROUS

Turbans rise in popularity, and are the perfect complement to the Chemise.

DRESSING WELL TAKES MORE TASTE THAN MONEY. A FEW CREATIVE TIPS:

◆ Try to get 2-piece outfits to avoid alteration costs.

◆ Purchase fake pearls with knots.

◆ Buy an inexpensive pair of gold and pearl earrings to spruce up a low-priced wardrobe.

◆ Store your clothes flat to preserve the shape.

◆ Stay away from tacky detailing.

Vivid Colors Are As Varied As A Rainbow, And Bold Combinations Are Acceptable. Try Wearing Black, Magenta, Red, Pink, Blue, White, Yellow, Turquoise, Green, Grey Or Orange, Mixing And Matching As You See Fit.

PASSINGS

Famed fashion designer Claire McCardell, creator of the "Popover" housedress, inventive sportswear styles and winner of the Coty American Fashion Critics' Award dies at age 52.

One of the most famous names in the history of fashion, Christian Dior, innovative originator of 1947's "New Look," dies at age 52.

1958

22-YEAR OLD YVES ST. LAURENT KEEPS THE DIOR NAME IN THE FOREFRONT OF FASHION WITH HIS TRAPEZE LINE OF DRESSES. HE TRIES TO LOWER HEMLINES, BUT THE PUBLIC SAYS NO.

Trapeze

Long Necklaces For The Back Look Divine With A Low Back Dress.

OUI, THESE ARE FROM PARIS

The new chemises are given more form-fitting shapes than their predecessors, adding elegance to the often shapeless form. Designers are also showing one piece dresses that look like suits and two piece dresses.

WHEN IRISH EYES ARE A SMILIN'

EYEGLASSES ARE BIG, BIG, BIG AND CAN BE ROUND OR SQUARE. THE NEW PINHOLE GLASSES KEEP YOU RELAXED AS THEY KEEP OUT THE SUN.

WHAT GOES AROUND COMES AROUND, OR, HAVEN'T I SEEN THIS BEFORE?

FASHIONS FROM THE 1920'S ARE ONCE AGAIN IN VOGUE. THE VAMP DRESS, VAMP HAIRDO'S, VAMP MAKE-UP AND VAMP SHOES EMULATE LOOKS FROM A BYGONE ERA.

Shoe Biz...

PUT YOUR BEST FOOT FORWARD WITH TEXTURED SHOES, POINTY TOES, T-STRAPS AND TALL HEELS.

Plastic Heel Taps Silently Protect Your Shoes.

Shoes Are Adorned With Stripes, Paisley And Other Patterns And Can Be Wildly Colorful.

Footwear Materials Include Mohair, Velveteen, Satin Suede And Leather.

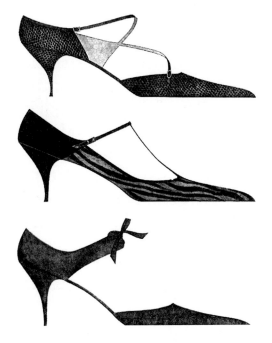

AC•CEN•TU•ATE
THE AC•CES•SOR•IES

Leotights In A Variety Of Colors Worn Alone Or Under Shorts, Skirts And The New Jumpsuits.

Gloves With Up To Ten Buttons

Long Handbags

Turquoise, Sapphire, Pearl, Beaded, Crystal & Diamond Jewelry

Chiffon Scarves

Seamless Stockings

Bows On Dresses, Hats, Jackets, Coats & Shoes

A few owners of the most beautiful baubles in the United States are: Mrs. Merriweather Post, Mrs. Horace Dodge, Sr., Mrs. Alfred I. du Pont, Mrs. Eleanor Searle Whitney, Mrs. William B. Leeds, Helena Rubenstein, Doris Duke, Baroness Barbara Hutton von Cramm, Sonia Henie, Mrs. Buddy Rogers (Mary Pickford) and The Duchess of Windsor.

WHAT A YEAR IT WAS!

As Clothing Stays Whimsical, Perfume Become Full-Bodied And Dramatic

HOT TO TROT, LOVE YOUR DOTS

Polka Dots In All Sizes Adorn Your Daytime Or Evening Dresses.

105,000 GARMENT INDUSTRY WORKERS GO ON STRIKE.

COTY AMERICAN
FASHION CRITICS' AWARD
– The "Winnie"
ARNOLD SCASSI

COTY AMERICAN
FASHION CRITICS'
HALL OF FAME AWARD
Posthumously Awarded To
CLAIRE McCARDELL

NEIMAN-MARCUS
AWARD FOR
DISTINGUISHED SERVICE
YVES ST. LAURENT

WHAT A YEAR IT WAS!

SPRING FASHION UNVEILED IN ENGLAND

These ladies are all a-buzz about their latest bonnets.

Buyers from all over the world get to see this nylon petti-brief being introduced to England.

"Pink Champagne" is the name of this model made of elaborate netting and tiny flowers and calls for a hefty checkbook.

This inverted eggcup shaped hat sits back on the head.

This light wool fleece suit with a cropped jacket is slightly belted in the back.

This pale pink straw hat is called "The Windsock" and one can clearly see the Dutch influence.

Milady would have to think twice before wearing this stunning pale yellow head-turner to a matinee performance.

WHAT A YEAR IT WAS!

LOOK AT DAT HAT

* Fringe Feathered
* Pillbox
* Cloche
* Pate
* Breton
* Slouch
* Eggcup
* Beret
* Feathers

SUIT UP

Choices for this year's loveliest suits include the dress and jacket combo, high waists, cropped jackets, long jackets, narrow jackets, telescoped jackets, ripple skirts, narrow skirts, and pleated skirts.

Magic Words For Coats Are Mohair, Twill, Wool And Fleece.

Hair

The Vamp Coiffure, Maintained By A Colorful Band, Is Worn With A Vamp Dress.

Short And Layered, With Highlights.

"Happy Hair" Is A New Conditioner That Can Be Sprayed On.

Gold Streaks – Choose Your Favorite Carat – Add Natural Looking Color.

The Pinwheel Cut, Bouffant And Pageboy Are Stylish.

The Cloche-Coif With A Side Part And Barretts Is Fashionable With Young Women.

Wigs Are A Great Way To Change Your Look With Ease – And Only Need To Be Cleaned Every Few Weeks. Nylon Wigs Cost The Same As A Good Hat, While Wigs Made Of Real Hair Begin At $175. Wild Wig Colors Include Pink And Green.

Make Up

Lips Are Luscious When Painted In Bright Red, Pink Or Orange.

24-Carat Gold Is Added To One Brand Of Lipstick For A Nighttime Shimmer.

Eyebrow Pencils Used In Place Of Traditional Eye Shadows Stays On Longer. Other Eye-Catching Looks Include Eyebrows With A Curved Arch To Make Eyes Appear Larger And False Eyelashes.

Healthy Complexions Become Flawless With A Liquid Foundation That Contains A Moisturizer To Protect Skin Through The Day.

MEN'S WEAR

The New Continental Look Features The Bowler Hat, A Two Button Sportscoat And Cuff-Free Pants.

The Straw Boater Is Summer's Prevalent Hat.

A Golf Jacket Is The First Garment To Be Fastened With Velcro.

Other Popular Men's Styles Include High-Buttoned Jackets, Flared Coats And Wide-Bottomed Pants.

The Ivy League Look Of Tapered And Pleatless Trousers And Suits With Narrow Lapels And Natural Shoulders Remains Widespread On And Off Campus.

Select Cufflinks Have Thermometers, Barometers And Compasses Inside Helping The Well-Dressed Man Become The Well-Informed Man.

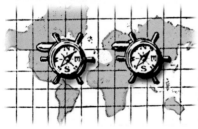

Country Wear Includes Jackets With Vents And Slanted Pockets, Comfortable For Riding Or Milling About The Countryside.

Whether you are dashing across town or flying cross-country you can always feel sure of being well-dressed in Hart Schaffner & Marx clothes. They are distinctive and in perfect taste. They are made in a wide selection of fabrics ranging from the quiet tones so popular today to brighter fabrics, rich in color and design. Here is one of the new notes —muted stripes…shadowy, quiet and handsome.

Suit shown is faultlessly tailored in the famous slim, trim "Trend" model perfected by H S & M. See Hunt & Winterbotham British flannel, or HS&M's own American classic, the Eton Flannel suit. Muted stripes also in wide variety of worsteds.

HART SCHAFFNER & MARX

THE NAME THAT MEANS SO MUCH TO SO MANY WELL-DRESSED MEN

SPORTS

The World Series

The New York Yankees win the World Series.

New York becomes the first team in 33 years to win the World Series after trailing 3 games to 1.

New York's Ebbets Field And Polo Grounds Empty As Baseball Season Opens

The gloom of New York fans is matched by the jubilation of fans out west as San Francisco welcomes the Giants *(left)* while Los Angeles turns out to welcome the Dodgers *(right)*.

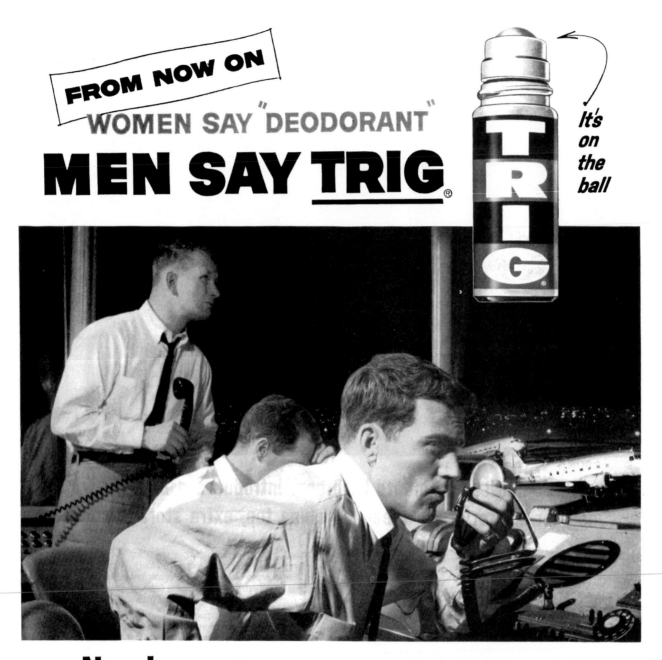

FROM NOW ON

WOMEN SAY "DEODORANT"

MEN SAY TRIG.

It's on the ball

Now! A <u>man's</u> way to check perspiration odor
—goes on in seconds...works for 24 hours!

● Trig is a man's product—the scent, the color, the works! Goes on a man's way—rolls on in seconds!

● Trig goes right to work—underarm hair can't block it out. Trig delivers positive protection—man-size protection that lasts right around the clock.

● Trig isn't messy like a cream! Trig doesn't trickle like a spray! And Trig is not a crumbly stick!

● Trig is for the 6 men out of 10 who now use a deodorant—and for the 4 out of 10 who've been holding out for a <u>man's</u> way to check perspiration odor!

ANOTHER FINE PRODUCT OF BRISTOL-MYERS

Baseball

New York Yankees Win The World Series Regaining The World Championship By Beating Milwaukee 4-3

- During the sixth game of the World Series, the Braves' **Hank Aaron** advances to second base after a first base collision with Yankee first baseman Bill Skowron as Skowron attempts to field a bad throw from pitcher Art Ditman.

- The Brooklyn Dodgers become the Los Angeles Dodgers while the New York Giants become the San Francisco Giants as the West Coast becomes home to two major league teams for the first time.

- Dodger catcher **Roy Campanella** is paralyzed from the neck down in a car crash.

- **Roy Campanella's** "Campy's Corner," a five minute interview show on New York station WINS, begins taping from his hospital room with Dodger teammates Pee Wee Reese and Jackie Robinson as his first guests.

- Boston's **Ted Williams** hits woman in head with hurled bat after strikeout.

Home Run Kings

National League
Ernie Banks (Chicago)

American League
Mickey Mantle (New York)

RBI Leaders

National League
Ernie Banks (Chicago)

American League
Jackie Jensen (Boston)

Batting Champions

National League
Richie Ashburn (Philadelphia)

American League
Ted Williams (Boston)

Most Valuable Player

National League
Ernie Banks (Chicago)

American League
Jackie Jensen (Boston)

Rookie Of The Year

National League
Orlando Cepeda (San Francisco)

American League
Albie Pearson (Washington)

Cy Young Award Winner

Bob Turley
(New York)

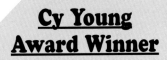

America's Carol Heiss Is Skating Queen Of The World

In Paris at the World Skating Championship, Carol Heiss, winner of the last two years defends her crown and dazzles the judges in the Free-Style.

The judges are unanimous awarding her the highest point score ever tallied by a woman—a near perfect performance for her third straight victory.

ICE SKATING

WORLD FIGURE SKATING CHAMPIONSHIP

Men:	**Dave Jenkins (U.S.)**
Women:	**Carol Heiss (U.S.)**

U.S. NATIONAL

Men:	**Dave Jenkins**
Women:	**Carol Heiss**

CANADIAN NATIONAL

Men:	**Charles Snelling**
Women:	**Margaret Crosland**

RIDING CLOTHES BY MILLER'S, NEW YORK

Pronounced America's most distinctive fine car

THE BOLD DISCERNING PEOPLE who launch all great changes in taste have chosen Imperial — decisively. In this magnificent car, they have found a crisp and wonderful distinction. A stirring sales record, ever mounting, underscores Imperial's ever-growing popularity.

The car itself is a styling masterpiece so fresh and so new that it even features gracefully curved sideglass, something you've never seen on any motorcar before.

And its performance? Incomparable. Take the wheel to see what the industry's finest engineering can do for you. See how your car, for all its impressive size and power, handles like silk. All driving strains are removed. At tight corners, sudden stops, your car floats perfectly level, supremely comfortable.

Claim — as the fine car that's right for you — the nation's acknowledged new style leader. See this beautiful new favorite, now at your Imperial Dealer's, in a wide choice of models and most attractive range of prices.

IMPERIAL . . . FINEST PRODUCT OF CHRYSLER CORPORATION

The triumphant

IMPERIAL

Finest expression of The Forward Look ⟩

161

1958

CAR RACING

WALTER HANSGEN, of Westfield, New Jersey, retains his national Class C modified sports car title winning more races than any other driver.

WORLD GRAND PRIX
MIKE HAWTHORNE
ENGLAND

WINSTON CUP
LEE PETTY

PRINCE RAINIER TROPHY

GUY MONRAISSE & JACQUES FERET
(Monaco's Robert Bertrand is killed when his car goes out of control.)

INDY 500

One of the most spectacular races in history is witnessed at the Memorial Day Indianapolis 500.

In the very first lap, the blazing pace resulted in a 13-car pileup killing veteran driver Patrick O'Connor.

The winner is Phoenix's Jimmy Bryan who reaches an average speed of almost 134 M.P.H. and gets a big congratulatory kiss.

WHAT A YEAR IT WAS!

BASKETBALL

NBA CHAMPIONSHIP
St. Louis Hawks Win Over Boston Celtics 4-2

★

NBA ANNUAL ALL-STAR GAME
The East Defeats The West 130-118

★

NCAA CHAMPIONS
University Of Kentucky Beats Seattle 84-72

NBA Scoring Leader ★	NBA Most Valuable Player ★	Player Of The Year ★	Rookie Of The Year ★	NBA All-Pro First Team ★
GEORGE YARDLEY Detroit (2,001 Points)	BILL RUSSELL Boston Celtics	ELGIN BAYLOR Seattle	WOODY SAULDSBERRY Philadelphia Warriors	GEORGE YARDLEY Detroit DOLPH SCHAYES Syracuse BOB PETTIT St. Louis BOB COUSY Boston BILL SHARMAN Boston

WILT CHAMBERLAIN SIGNS CONTRACT WITH HARLEM GLOBETROTTERS

Bowling

AMERICAN BOWLING SINGLES TITLE

ED SHAY
Chester, Pa.

Bowling Becomes The Nation's Fastest-Growing Sport Racking Up Big Profit Dollars

WHAT A YEAR IT WAS!

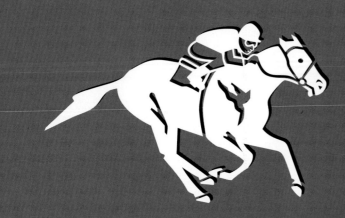

ISMAEL VALENZUELA Rides TIM TAM to Kentucky Derby And Preakness Wins.

EDDIE ARCARO Becomes The Third Jockey To Attain Over 4,000 Wins.

TIM TAM, #3 WINS THE KENTUCKY DERBY.

PASSINGS

National League baseball player for 17 years, **Chuck Klein**, 4 time league home-run champion and 1932's most valuable player dies at age 52.

Mel Ott, member of the New York Giants as both player and manager hit 511 home runs in his career, third highest in baseball's history, dies at age 49 from injuries sustained in a car accident.

"The Gray Eagle" **Tris Speaker**, holder of baseball's tenth highest batting average of .344, considered the greatest defensive outfielder the game has ever seen, major league player for over 22 years and once the highest paid player, dies at age 70.

Race car driver **Luigi Musso** dies at age 33 when his Ferrari crashes in the Grand Prix of France.

CHAMPIONS

TENNIS

U.S. LAWN TENNIS ASSOCIATION SINGLES

Men: Ashley Cooper (vs. Malcolm Anderson)
Women: Althea Gibson (vs. Darlene Hard)

WIMBLEDON

Men: Ashley Cooper (vs. Neale Fraser)
Women: Althea Gibson (vs. Angela Mortimer)

DAVIS CUP

United States 3, Australia 2

THE SOVIETS Make Their International Tennis Debut At The Fashionable Kent Championships In England With Two 17-Year Olds—ANNA DIMITRIEVA Of Moscow And ANDREI POTANIN Of Leningrad—Both Of Whom Are Beaten In The First Round.

CHESS

15-Year Old Bobby Fischer,
The Youngest Player
To Earn International Grand
Master Rating, Finishes Fifth In
The Candidates Chess
Tournament Held In Yugoslavia.

Mikhail Botvinnik
Retakes World
Chess Title.

WHAT A YEAR IT WAS!

1958 FOOTBALL

NFL CHAMPIONSHIP

In the first title game televised coast to coast, Johnny Unitas stars in the Baltimore Colts' sudden-death overtime victory over the New York Giants 23-17.

MOST VALUABLE PLAYER

Jim Brown (Cleveland)
His second year as a professional, Brown breaks the league record for number of yards gained rushing and ties it for number of touchdowns scored.

#1 NFL DRAFT CHOICE

King Hill QB
(Rice)

NFL SEASON LEADERS

Eddie LeBaron Passing
(Washington)
Raymond Berry
Receiving
(Baltimore)

HEISMAN TROPHY WINNER

Pete Dawkins HB
(U.S. Army)

CANADIAN FOOTBALL LEAGUE

Winnipeg Blue Bombers beat Hamilton Tigercats 35-28 for Grey Cup championship.

ALL-AMERICANS

Billy Cannon (LSU)
Pete Dawkins (Army)
Buddy Dial (Rice)

Louisiana State University football team rated the best in the U.S. by U.P.I. Coaches.

Louisiana's athletic segregation law ruled unconstitutional by 3-judge federal court in New Orleans.

Rose Bowl

Before a capacity crowd of 100,000 fans, Ohio State is champion beating Oregon 10-7.

With the Cleveland Browns leading 10-7, Bobby Joe Conrad gets ready to boot a long one for the Chicago Cardinals.

1.

Leroy Bolden takes it in the end zone and in a sensational sprint runs 102 yards to score.

2.

3.

Wearing #32, Cleveland's 228 pound Jim Brown receives the hand-off from Bobby Mitchell.

4.

Brown runs 41 yards for a touchdown followed by a thundering 68 yards for the fourth score and victory for the Browns 38-24.

5.

The fans go wild as the Browns win.

America's best-selling convertible
has the magic of the Thunderbird

Fabulous Thunderbird-inspired styling, mighty Thunderbird V-8 power and up to 12% easier steering are only part of the Sunliner's worth-more story.

For here's the "onliest" convertible in its field. The only one with top attached to roof supports so the top accordion-folds *itself* when lowered. The only convertible with *one* zipper across the rear window for the easiest operating, most foolproof rear window in its field. Yes, from fade-resistant top to exclusive vinyl-textured floor covering, Ford's Sunliner gives you the most in its field . . . the most rear leg-room, the most body mounts and the *most* for the very *least*. It's America's lowest priced convertible! Come in, see for yourself why Ford sells nearly *twice* as many convertibles as its nearest competitor.

nothing newer in the world
58 FORD

Like every Ford it has that Thunderbird touch. Coming or going—every beautifully sculptured line between the Sun-liner's Safety-Twin headlights and taillights has the dashing design of the breath-taking new Thunderbird!

BOXING CHAMPIONS

★ **HEAVYWEIGHT**
Floyd Patterson

★ **LIGHT HEAVYWEIGHT**
Archie Moore

★ **MIDDLEWEIGHT**
"Sugar" Ray Robinson regains Middleweight title for fifth time by defeating Carmen Basilio.

★ **WELTERWEIGHT**
Virgil Akins,
Don Jordan

★ **LIGHTWEIGHT**
Joe Brown

★ Five new members elected to the Boxing Hall of Fame:
Mike Gibbons
Tom Molineaux
Tommy Ryan
Ad Wolgast
Tony Zale

ICE HOCKEY

HART MEMORIAL TROPHY WINNER
(Most Valuable Player)
GORDIE HOWE
Detroit Red Wings

Montreal Canadiens Beat Boston Bruins 4-2 Winning The Stanley Cup

SOCCER

Brazil wins the World Cup beating Sweden 5-2 with **Pele**, king of soccer or the "Black Pearl" of the world's most popular sport, scoring two goals for Brazil in the final match.

WRESTLING

The Russian Wrestling squad, the first Soviet athletes to ever compete in the United States, establishes their superiority in the Olympic Freestyle version by beating America's AAU champions in Norman and Stillwater, Oklahoma.

WHAT A YEAR IT WAS!

America's Cup Yacht Race Revived After 21 Years

U.S. "Columbia" takes an early lead over Britain's challenger "Sceptre."

President Eisenhower is among the fans who gather in Newport, Rhode Island to witness the race for the cup, symbolic of Anglo-American rivalry.

The crew of the "Columbia" waves triumphantly as they win the race 4-0, once again keeping the cup in America where it's been without interruption since 1851.

WHAT A YEAR IT WAS!

GOLF

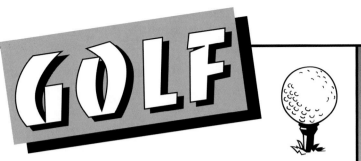

CYCLING

TOMMY BOLT WINS THE U.S. OPEN GOLF TOURNAMENT WITH A SCORE OF 283

The Winning Shot.

CHARLY GAUL wins Tour de France.

ATHLETE OF THE YEAR

MALE
Herb Elliott
(Track & Field)

FEMALE
Althea Gibson
(Tennis)

CHAMPIONS

World's Amateur Golf Council Is Organized.

U.S. MASTERS
Arnold Palmer
(First Masters' Win & PGA's Top Money Winner With $42,407.)

U.S. OPEN-Men
Tommy Bolt

U.S. OPEN-Women
Mickey Wright

U.S. GOLF ASSOCIATION
Charlie Coe

BRITISH OPEN
Peter Thomson

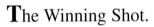

UCLA's student body president **Rafer Johnson** breaks the world Decathlon record and is later voted SPORTS ILLUSTRATED Sportsman Of The Year.

WHAT A YEAR IT WAS!

1958 ADVERTISEMENT

GREAT NEW IDEA FROM GULF! You can <u>restore clean-engine performance</u> with just one tankful of new Gulf Crest every 1,000 miles.

 New, advanced engines, of course, need new Gulf Crest as a full time fuel to maintain maximum engine performance. But . . .

 In other cars (cars not requiring highest octane gasoline), use a tankful of new Gulf Crest every 1,000 miles to *restore* clean-engine performance. New Gulf Crest neutralizes deposits left by other gasolines. You'll save on gasoline, spark plug replacements, costly engine servicing . . . and you'll begin to get that *live* power feeling again!

NEW GULF CREST
GASOLINE

172

At the Westminster Kennel Club's competition held at Madison Square Garden, Standard Poodle *"Puttencove Promise"* wins top dog honors, the first of his class to win since 1935.

CRICKET

The AMERICAN AMATEURS U.S. Cricket Team proves their superiority over their English counterparts, The LORD'S TAVERNERS, winning 133-132 as bands from both sides play on the sidelines. The prize? A cup of Boston tea leaves.

Pakistani cricket team tours the United States.

TRACK SENSATION OF THE YEAR

AAU mile champion 20-year old Australian **Herb Elliot** sets new mark in Dublin All-Star Race finishing in 3 minutes, 54 1/2 seconds.

Hayes W. Jones sets record of 7.1 seconds in the 60-yard high hurdles at the AAU National Championships held in Madison Square Garden.

FENCING

In the world championships tournament held at the University of Pennsylvania in Philadelphia, the U.S.S.R. wins the Prince of Monaco Trophy for the best over-all results.

1958 WAS A GREAT YEAR, BUT...

Charles Cooley

Reindeer Magic

Will Santa's Reindeer Find You?

Illustrated by
Brenda Lyons

KAVIK
PUBLISHING

Reindeer Magic

Copyright © 2010 by Charles Cooley

All Rights Reserved.

Published by KAVIK Publishing

Printed in China by BookMasters, Inc.
Kowloon, Hong Kong
Printed August, 2010
Reference Number A26

Age Group - 4 to 9 years.

Library of Congress Cataloging-in-Publication Data

No part of this publication may be reproduced, or stored

in a retrieval system, or transmitted in any form or by any

means - electronic, mechanical, photocopy, recording, or any

other form - without written permission of the publisher.

Requests for more information should be addressed to:

P.O. Box 4787, Canton, Georgia 30114

Artwork designs are reproduced under license from

KAVIK Publishing, Canton, Georgia, and may not be

reproduced without permission. For more information

regarding art prints featured in this book, please contact:

KAVIK Publishing, P. O. Box 4787, Canton, Georgia 30114

or www.kavikpublishing.com.

ISBN - 978-0-615-34143-9

To: _____

From: _____

Date: _____

Not long ago on a dark winter's night
in the deepest woods of Montana, Amy
Johansen was very busy . . . .
writing her letter to
Santa Claus.

She had written letters to Santa before, but this year was especially important. In all of her years, she had never been so afraid of missing Christmas, or actually . . . . . of Santa Claus missing her.

Just two months ago, Amy and her family had moved from their native country of Denmark to the strange but beautiful land of Montana. Montana was different from any place Amy had ever seen before. There were no colorful sailboats, no nearby playgrounds, and certainly no close friends. Amy's Dad could see the sadness in her big blue eyes. He loved her so much that he tried to make this new place like the home she so terribly missed. He even hung a rope swing on the big oak tree in their front yard. It looked exactly like the one she had in Denmark, but it just wasn't the same.

$\mathcal{A}$s she looked out from this lonely mountaintop onto acres and acres of trees, she could barely see the lights of a small town many miles away. Her brother Josh, who was very brave, did his best to reassure his little sister. Santa was sure to know that they had moved, he told her, and of course, he knew about this land called Montana.

*B*ut, as Christmas Eve approached, even Josh began to worry. That night after dinner, the kids had heard their Dad say that the next day's trip to town would probably be his last until after Christmas.

With so little time and so much to do, Amy and Josh rushed up to Amy's room to finish their letters to Santa. They had been working on their letters for weeks, always one more thing to add or adjust . . . . . but tonight was their last chance!

he next morning, Mom and Dad were surprised as the two authors made their way downstairs early for breakfast with tired eyes and letters in hand. Mom helped with the postage, and longing stares followed their father as he made his way down the drive-way. He was holding their

last hope of Santa

finding them.

From: Tosh
From: Amy

Santa Claus
North Pole

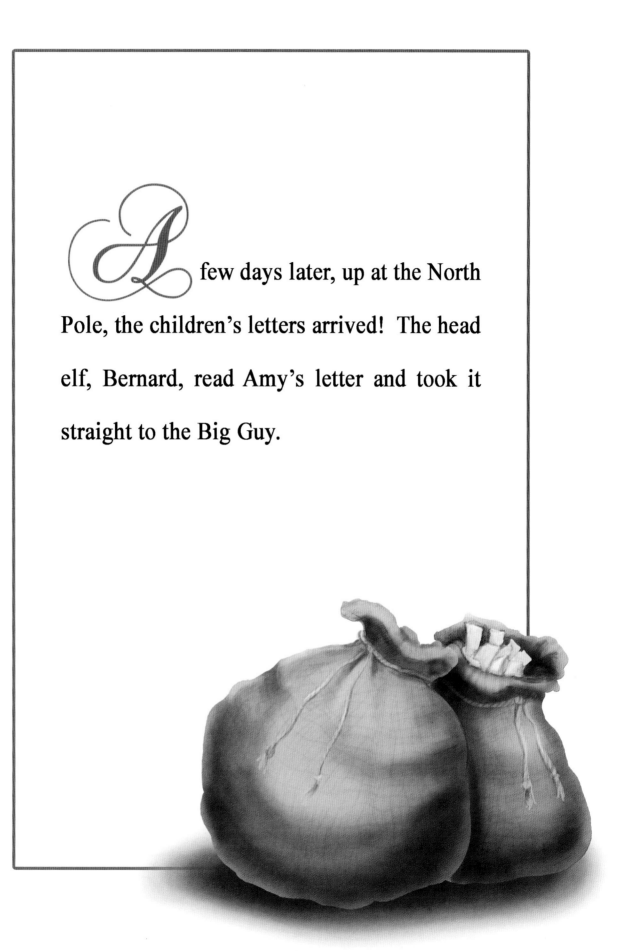

$\mathscr{A}$ few days later, up at the North Pole, the children's letters arrived! The head elf, Bernard, read Amy's letter and took it straight to the Big Guy.

Bernard found Santa sitting in his giant old wooden chair, a chair that was worn from many years of reading children's letters. Though he was not sure at first, Bernard knew he had done the right thing when he saw a tear twinkle in the corner of Santa's eye. Santa could sense the fear and loneliness of this hopeful little girl. He had already marked their new home on his route months before, but he knew that something extra special had to be done or Amy and her brother would worry until Christmas Eve.

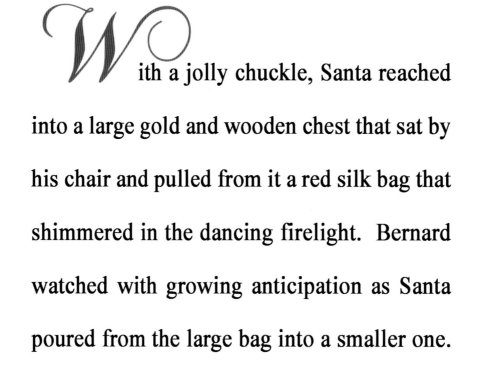

With a jolly chuckle, Santa reached into a large gold and wooden chest that sat by his chair and pulled from it a red silk bag that shimmered in the dancing firelight. Bernard watched with growing anticipation as Santa poured from the large bag into a smaller one.

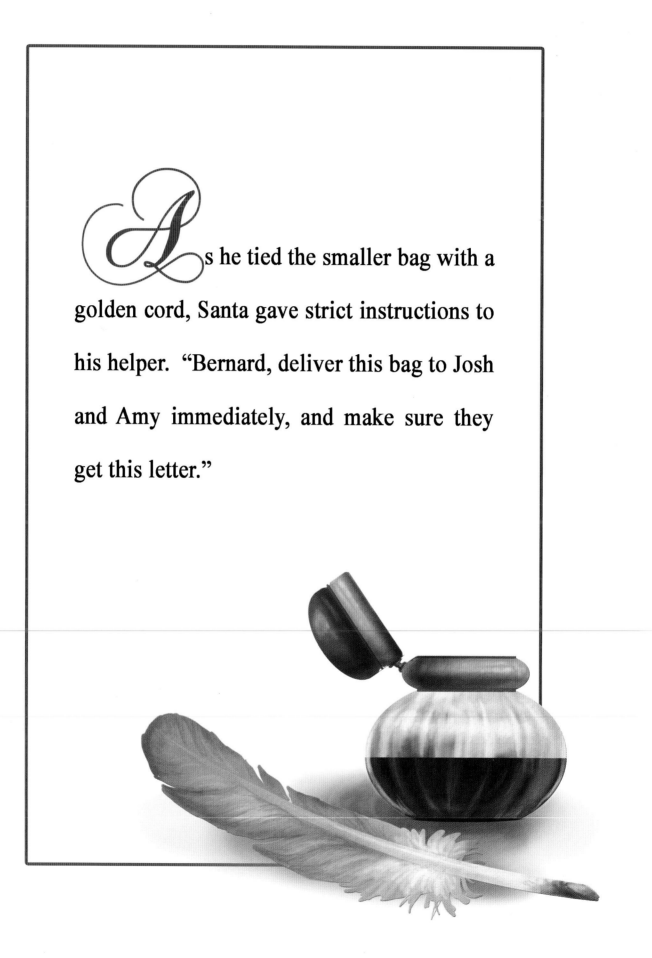

*A*s he tied the smaller bag with a golden cord, Santa gave strict instructions to his helper. "Bernard, deliver this bag to Josh and Amy immediately, and make sure they get this letter."

In this bag is a special mixture of Christmas oats and Reindeer Magic, which is what makes my reindeer fly. On Christmas Eve, sprinkle this onto the yard in front of your house. The smell of the oats and special ingredients in the Reindeer Magic will guide my reindeer straight to your door.

Love, Santa

S ilently peering between the branches of the big oak tree in Josh and Amy's yard, Bernard smiled at the confused look on their mother's face and the glee of the children as they picked up the little bag he had so carefully placed on their front porch.

*O*n Christmas Eve, the freshly fallen snow barely covered the Reindeer Magic Amy and Josh had so carefully spread over the front yard. As the sleigh crossed over the mountains, Santa could hardly hold the reigns as the reindeer headed straight for this little home so deep in the Montana woods.

The End

Acknowledgement

I would like to thank the many people who made this undertaking possible. First, thanks to Joshua and Caleb for being my inspiration from the very beginning. Also, to my lovely wife, Beth, for her patience and understanding to allow me the freedom to spend so much time and money to make my dreams come true.

I was fortunate enough to find a team of people who were willing to spend the countless hours required to make this book possible. A special thanks to Sandie Kimbrel and Rhonda Kerns for their insight and knowledge that made this project better than I ever expected.

Dedication

This book is dedicated to Ruth Thomas Cooley. She was kind to all, even when they didn't deserve it. A "Christ-like" spirit was lived out in her life on a daily basis. She was born and raised in a small house on the eastern side of Atlanta, Georgia. From my earliest memories, my Mom was always making Christmas special for all of us. From her cooking cornbread and pecan pies, to the smile on her face, no matter what happened or what the rest of us did (good or frequently bad), Mom showed unconditional love. Like the mortar in a brick wall, she was the glue that held the family together. She never wanted the focus to be on her. She was always behind the scenes working so very hard to make everyone else enjoy themselves.

As I sat at my desk writing this story, the joy and love that this beautiful lady had given me was what I wanted to pass on to my children and the generations of children to come. Every holiday season, when I sit in front of the Christmas tree in the quiet of the night, I am thankful for the many blessings that have been given by those who sacrificed so much for me. This one is for you, Mom, or actually, because of you.

Love, Charles

Reindeer Magic Instructions:

In this bag is a special mixture of Christmas oats and Reindeer Magic, which is what makes my reindeer fly. On Christmas Eve, sprinkle this onto the yard in front of your house. The smell of the oats and special ingredients in the Reindeer Magic will guide my reindeer straight to your door.

Love, Santa